To Donna Allan
with best wishes
"Food for Thought"

December 2004

Canada
Enroute to Prosperity

Volker Thomsen

Epic
Press

Belleville, Ontario, Canada

Canada Enroute to Prosperity

Copyright © 2004, Volker Thomsen

ISBN: 1-55306-879-3
LSI Edition: 1-55306-887-4

**For more information or
to order additional copies, please contact:**

www.volkerthomsen.com

Epic Press is an imprint of *Essence Publishing,* a Christian Book Publisher
dedicated to furthering the work of Christ through the written word. For more
information, contact:
20 Hanna Court, Belleville, Ontario, Canada K8P 5J2
Phone: 1-800-238-6376 • Fax: (613) 962-3055
E-mail: publishing@essencegroup.com • Internet: www.essencegroup.com

Printed in Canada
by

Epic
Press

Table of Contents

Preface 7
Acknowledgements 11
About the Author 13

Section 1: A Vision of Canada Enroute to Prosperity
1. Canada Now 17
2. A Picture of Canada Enroute to Prosperity 27
3. What are Canada's Greatest Challenges
    and Opportunities? 49
4. Preparing Canadians to Lead Industrial Innovation
    in All Areas, Including Housing, Transportation,
    Energy and Communication 69
5. Canada Is Far Behind in Developing Green
    and/or Renewable Energy .89
6. Innovation is Always Driven by Learning
    and Education 107
7. Creating a Healthy Balance between Urban
    and Rural Development 125
8. Necessary Changes for Creating an Innovation
    Strategy for Canadian Business 131

9.   Bibliocentre: A Model for the Digital Library for
     the Canadian Future 137
10. Apprenticeship Training the Traditional Way and
     Apprenticeship Training Embedded in a
     Co-op Diploma 145
11. Developing a Humane Policy on Immigration 161

     Summary 177

Section 2: Food for Thought
     A Preamble and Foreword by the Author 181

12. Life Is Only Worth Living In Healthy
     Surroundings 185
13. Nutrition a Hundred Years Ago and
     Nutrition Today 195
14. The Farming Industry Today 205
15. Connections Between the Environment, Nutrition,
     Hereditary Characteristics and Addictions 233
16. A Practical Guide for Changing Over to
     Whole Foods 241
17. Important Information About Our Basic
     Nutritional Substances 247
18. Losing Weight Without Hunger Pains and
     Resignation—Made Easy—Without
     Negative Results 261
19. Environmental and Agricultural Reform 269
20. Guidance for the Changeover to High Quality
     Wholesome Food 279

     A Short Summary 303

"It's not the strongest of species who survive,
nor the most intelligent
but the ones most responsive to change."
Charles Darwin

Preface

This book is dedicated to our political leaders, to encourage the introduction of long overdue changes. The turbulent Canadian political scene creates major challenges but equally tremendous opportunities. Our newly appointed Prime Minister Paul Martin and his minority government can relate to the new power players, like Dalton McGuinty, Jean Charest and others, along with their respective governments, in a co-operative way. Hopefully the opportunity will be utilized. This book is equally dedicated to the opposition members, who under the leadership of Steven Harper, Gilles Duceppe and Jack Layton have a historic opportunity to inspire and support change, whether as the official opposition, a coalition, or a supporting partner.

Once the political waters have calmed somewhat, Paul Martin's accommodating personality may even induce some of the opposition parties or members to get on board for this exciting voyage to an overdue political renewal and to new economic, social and cultural horizons. Ralph Klein's Alberta government is leading on the renewable energy front, and its commitment to purchase 90 percent of its power needs in the form of renewable energy should be an inspiration to other premiers and particularly to Paul Martin's minority government.

In many countries, including Canada, it has been proven that under minority governments and coalitions there can be periods of increased change and innovation and more productive co-operation than under majority governments. While Canada may not have a rich history of forming coalitions over longer periods, sound coalitions in many societies have produced some of the best results that governments can achieve.

Section 1: Innovation for Canada

In creating an innovative Canadian approach, we could lead our nation and the world to an industrial, social, economic and cultural renewal.

We want to understand our key health care challenges as opportunities for introducing an increased focus on preventative medicine, improving lifestyles and teaching our youngest citizens these means of avoiding chronic illness, thus reducing the need for increasing services and escalating costs.

Dealing properly with energy use and the environment and focusing on renewable/green energy could lead to the creation of hundreds of thousands of new jobs.

Because of Canada's size, transportation and communication of any kind plays a major role. We should therefore inspire and help the automotive, automotive parts, communications, IT and microelectronics industries to create new and innovative products. Because of our harsh climate, better-designed and -insulated homes should utilize alternative sources of energy. In particular, innovative management of water and waste water offers unlimited opportunities for expansion.

Access to education, training and skills acquisition should be created under the umbrella of provincial leadership, but federal policies and standards need to be in place so that all Canadians have the opportunity to show the world we can be competitive with other leading innovative industrial nations, like those in Scandinavia, Europe and Asia.

Canada is known for its friendly people and as a vast and beautiful land. We should not allow Canada to drift in the direction of mediocrity! Let us also make Canada known for being a leader in innovation and learning, where opportunities and development are linked to the whole population in a holistic way. Let us embrace innovation and renewal.

Section 2: Food for Thought

"Food for Thought" deals with parts of a revised and updated extract of my original book that was written in support of Michael Gorbachev's reforms in the Soviet Union.

Perestroika, Our Environment and Food for the World was originally published in 1988 in Germany, Denmark and Russia, in German, Danish and Russian.

This includes an updated inspiration to "Canada Eat and Live Smart." I renamed it "Food for Thought" after the translation into English and revision.

"Food for Thought" is a documentation of today's challenges and opportunities. Pollution of the environment, the waste of energy, unnatural nutrition, lack of sport, civilization diseases and drug addictions are problems of our time. Hereto, I offer a few practical solutions.

This part is a basic introduction to an optimal nutrition and lifestyle to help you to improve and maintain your health. At the end of part two I share information and numerous personal recipes to get you going.

Have fun!

Acknowledgements

I want to thank all the kind people who helped me during the final stage of putting this very substantial document together and who enabled me to finish this project in spite of my very demanding schedule as the leader of St. Lawrence College.

A special thank you goes to my dear wife, Li, who as a returning student, a mother and a housewife has an equally demanding schedule and yet has never stopped supporting me.

My editors Carole Morrison, David Chescoe, Lori Mackay and my daughter Andrea deserve to be recognized. They made sure that my numerous mistakes were reduced to a minimum. They put a lot of hours into the project and shared my passion and commitment.

My assistant, Andrea, helped me write the two energy papers, and her cheerful understanding was, as always, an anchor in our very diversified and quickly changing environment.

Gord MacDougall's helping hand to overcome some of my technical hurdles in the battle with my computer was also very appreciated.

About the Author

Volker Thomsen assumed his duties as President and CEO of St. Lawrence College on October 1, 2000. In September 2004 St. Lawrence College Board of Governors appointed Volker Thomsen for a second five-year term, from 2005 to 2010.

Volker Thomsen, a resident of Kingston since 1999, has more than 30 years experience as a successful founder, shareholder and CEO of a group of companies in the food, natural health products, pharmaceutical manufacturing and marketing sectors. He has, furthermore, during the same period been involved in renewable energy, particularly in Denmark and Germany. He participated in planning wind parks in conjunction with biomass reactors, enabling rural communities to combine energy in a meaningful way and be independent of outside supplies. At the same time, the environment was relieved of the negative effects of using too much manure for fertilizer. Thomsen has also been actively engaged in music and in the arts, both in Europe and in Canada. In this capacity he is also the visionary behind the "Festival on the St. Lawrence." This international festival in Northern New York and Eastern Ontario is focused on music, art and heritage on both sides of the river.

Volker Thomsen has worked in his international businesses located in Denmark, Norway, Sweden, Finland, Holland, Belgium, Germany, Canada, England, France, Spain, U.S.A., Denmark, Ireland, Saudi Arabia, Nigeria, Jamaica, Columbia, Hong Kong and China. In addition to founding numerous successful international companies, Thomsen has for many years participated on the boards of these companies as a director and as a shareholder. He was also a leading director of a small co-operative bank in his hometown Flensburg, an old Danish city on the German/Danish border, and remained on its supervisory board for fifteen years.

Volker Thomsen's interest in education and training began early in his career when he taught international trade and economics. He has been involved in adult education in its many different facets during his career and in 1989 was certified by the German certification authority as a teacher/educator of apprentices and managers. Having experienced apprenticeship training first-hand, Thomsen is a strong advocate for apprenticeship programs, vocational programs and community colleges in Canada. He is a member of the Ontario MTCU (Ministry of Training, Colleges and Universities) Training Branch Steering Committee for Reforming Apprenticeships, where he has participated in reforming apprenticeships and in creating a Co-op Diploma Apprenticeship program, an innovate new approach.

An avid sailor, Volker Thomsen lives on one of the Thousand Islands near Kingston with his wife and two children.

A Vision of Canada Enroute to Prosperity

Chapter One

Canada Now

Our Heritage

Building on the richness of the Canadian society, including all aspects of our cultural and social heritage, we need to include the First Nations' and New Nations' culture and heritage as a very important—maybe the most important—part of the foundation upon which Canada was built and will continue to build.

As a child growing up in Europe, I read dozens of books about the history of Native Americans. Some of the books showed the romantic side, others the real picture, including the merciless cruelty of the European conquest and the near extinction of hundreds of First Nations people. After forty years of living in Canada with long overseas stays in between, I have learned to look at it from both a Canadian and a global viewpoint.

Even if Canada is faring much better than the rest of the Americas, this is the darkest spot of our history. It will take a lot of healing before the affected First and New Nations will be able to live together in full harmony, integrated in a united Canada.

However, as a nation we have put it on the agenda in a sincere way, and our political leaders will have to show great leadership to deal with this in a respectful and appropriate fashion. It is encouraging that all parties acknowledge that we need to evolve out of this, strengthened and ready to face the challenges of today's world, with a great vision for joint goals in a shared future.

This will mean navigating a fine line. Whatever we can and will do may be too little or too much. We do not want to burden the future with an obligation similar to our bilingual status, which in reality we cannot live up to and has not given the results we were looking for. These sensitive areas are some of the many sacred cows that I will be referring to. Some we will be able to eliminate; others will remain. The future can still be bright if we, with mutual respect, focus on and realize our dreams and our opportunities.

Our Neighbours, our Governance and our Social Values

In this section I will discuss Canada's dependence on the U.S. market and a few economic facts. Why are Canadian values so different from U.S. values? Our society, which besides the First Nations consists of many cultures and includes many new immigrants, has been defined by numerous great Canadians, who tried to create a new world of values and a different point of view. Our ambitions are very different from U.S. ambitions. Therefore our policies, and particularly our social and foreign policy, cannot by any means be compared to those of the U.S.A.

We do not want to be the world's police, just as we do not want to be a society of very rich and very poor. Therefore we will need to go our own way. Because of this it will likely be easier to co-operate with Democratic than with Republican U.S. administrations. However, if our Conservatives and Liberals together with the other parties could formulate common Canadian values and create a clear foreign policy, our administration would not have to do the splits when dealing with U.S.A. or international relations.

Canada has also the unique First Nation's background, with a diversified long history and experience in peacemaking and peacekeeping. It is therefore not by coincidence but definitely by choice that we prefer to be involved only in peace missions.

Education

We can be proud of how far we have come in our educational system. In spite of its shortfalls, we do have great diversity; we are committed as a society to preserving the right to a universal education; and we have open access to education that promotes lifelong learning. We do, of course, have the same hurdles as any nation.

In a rapidly changing world, it is very difficult to keep up with evolution. Things that were the right things to implement a hundred years ago may be completely out of question today, just as steps taken under Diefenbaker, Pearson or even Trudeau may not be appropriate today. A lot of new ideas were introduced in the Trudeau era and, as before, some are sustainable; others have already outlived themselves.

Within education we are doing well, and yet we are struggling to create proper pathways for the various talents and gifts of our citizens. In addition, we are particularly struggling with training and enabling our students to use self-discipline and accept responsibility.

Freedom and rights can only be preserved if we take on responsibility. The best health-service system can only be maintained if we take responsibility for our own health and do not demand that society do that for us. In a way we have gone from one extreme to the next in both health care and education. It is therefore quite understandable that we still are struggling. The moment we as a social society grow up and change our demanding attitude to one of appreciation, we will do much better. The right to an education is a great privilege, with the obligation also to utilize opportunities by performing to the best of our abilities. The same rule applies to all human rights. Whenever we are misusing society's generosity without being made accountable, without returning anything, it will have a backfiring effect.

Having this in mind, it will be much easier to define the needed policies and the missing pathways. For example, look at the new policy created by Dalton McGuinty that ensures that all students have to remain in school until the age of eighteen. We can applaud this if we can ensure that the students will support it and benefit, but if the students are going to just hang around a little longer without any achievements, it will be another great expense and waste.

Health Care

It is not surprising that health is our greatest challenge at this moment in our history. Almost two hundred years of industrialization has greatly changed our world. Our bodies don't have the same ability to change or the ability to adapt to refined, denatured products without being damaged.

The environment is struggling; our diet has changed dramatically; and we do not get enough physical exercise. At the same time, the social conscience is improving and the exploitation of labour is coming to an end. However, industrialization has also created an economic system and media that controls, if not manipulates, our behaviour. We are eating and drinking processed products, which have made life easier but are challenging our health.

We are in a transition period where our knowledge level as well as our physical level is limping behind the fast pace of development of a world of new products. Therefore the term *health care*, which should mean *taking care of our health*, is misused for solutions for our sicknesses instead of for preventing illness in the first place. Therefore the present health care system is really a "sick care" system.

When we educate ourselves enough to build the missing link between prevention and curing or healing, then we will be able to adjust ourselves to live a healthy and balanced life in a modern industrial society. We must therefore link education to health care, and we must start with children as young as possible.

When we read the Fraser Mustard Report on early childhood (www.founders.net), it becomes obvious that it is crucial to focus on the beginning years. The United Way campaign "Success by Six" is one good step for creating awareness and support for the most vulnerable period of life. Care for the developing fetus, the baby and the early child is by far the best health care we can apply. This will also create awareness and knowledge in the young family and in society as to what needs to be done to stay healthy and happy. A focus on informing and educating future generations at all school levels will automatically follow. Therefore investing into education and into the beginning stages of life will avoid many mistakes that have created the never-ending, growing demand on health care.

It is, of course, difficult for our political leaders to get out of this vicious circle. They are caught in the trap of the necessity to satisfy their electorate's demand for immediate solutions and at the same time do proper long-range planning. Both things need to be done at this moment, and every penny invested into education and information will eventually return manifold. I address this issue in greater detail in "Canada Eat and Live Smart" in the chapter "What are Canada's Greatest Challenges and Opportunities" This study will show you that educating ourselves will soon bring a reduction in health costs, a long overdue turnaround, to the benefit of all the other areas that have had to be neglected because of the never-ending escalation of health care spending, at the growth rate of 4 to 8 percent per year.

Our Environment and Our Resources

As humans we will only earn the right to exist if we start to respect the environment we are part of. We are giving lip service and endorsing the Kyoto Accord. At the same time, we still continue to be the biggest polluters on earth and take it as our right to use or misuse our resources as we please. It will take much more than lip service to undo the damage we have done. Here again, it will take a change in attitude; we need to appreciate the great privilege it is to live in a vast and rich country like Canada. If we don't appreciate the grand nature and the magnificent creation we are part of, we will ultimately lose it. The privilege to live in a free country like Canada is something we better appreciate and be proud of.

As a very valuable source of information and direction into a better future, I recommend that you read the background document for the Green Power Workshop Series 2003/4 by Pollution Probe and Summerhill Group, at www.pollutionprobe.org.

My policy paper "Without true leadership and ownership alternative energies will not succeed: The need for policy creation and renewal at the federal, provincial and municipal levels" (SESCI 2003 Queens University), included in this book under "Canada is far behind in developing green and/or renewable energy," will also give a well-rounded overview of the 2003 situation.

Historic First Nations' Values and Principles Can Evolve as Part of Canadian Values

Three years ago, in partnership with First Nations Peoples in the U.S.A. and Canada, I started to participate in creating one of the first traditional Haudenoshaunee universities. It was clear from the beginning that this learning circle must build on traditional values and language.

There are five areas in particular where the old First Nations' values can help us to define and lead Canada into the future:

• Governance led by the elders and living in harmony together

• Learning by doing

• Natural medicine and traditional lifestyle

• Living in tune with the environment

• Peacekeeping

These traditional values can be a part of our modern industrial society's thinking. We tend to believe that traditional thinking or values do not mix well with our modern age with its many new developments. That is actually a misunderstanding; values have in reality never changed and will never change. The way we interpret these will of course vary, based on the time we live in, our point of view, our background and our beliefs.

It is interesting to notice that more and more official functions and conferences start out using elders from the First Nations to bless the gathering and encourage a positive outcome. Some of us not familiar with the thinking and the habits of our native brothers and sisters and their elders have certain difficulties in participating in this very inclusive way. The swearing-in ceremony of the new Paul Martin cabinet, hosted by Governor General Adrienne Clarkson and her husband John Ralston Saul in Rideau Hall, showed how values and habits of our First Nations can be easily integrated into our modern society's celebrations.

The five areas of fundamental values mentioned above have for thousands of years played a large role in the lives and survival of this country's First Nations. These values made it possible for hundreds of First Nations in all of America to build thriving societies of more than one hundred million people and to live in relative peace for very long periods.

Unfortunately, the dramatic impact of the European immigration led to the extinction of many great nations. However a small group of First Nations are surviving, and, as ironic as it may sound, they are presently the only group in Canada with real growth in birthrates (www.hc-sc.gc.ca). Many seem to be gradually overcoming the major hurdles our Western society has created for them. We can see the beginning of a revival and a great opportunity to do a lot of physical and spiritual healing, followed by overcoming the past.

The way things are going, there is a great opportunity for the First Nations to take a very positive and important role in shaping the future of our country. Their values and traditions may well be able to help them recover and to help our young Canadian nation find its own way in a modern struggling world of many differences.

The Canadian Way of Life

Most people on earth are quite insecure in their lives, in the political and economical structure of their societies or countries, and in the integrity and ability of their leaders.

This is, and sounds, devastating and could well end up in an uncontrollable situation where our existence is threatened, regardless of where we live. Politically, economically and spiritually we are at a turning point. The unique Canadian way of life, which developed into a socialistic society with certain capitalistic values and embraces many cultures, can well be at the beginning of a new era.

Similar clusters are evolving in different locations, such as New Zealand, Australia, the UK, Scandinavia, Germany, the Netherlands, Belgium, Luxembourg, parts of Eastern Europe and many more. They all have in common that they are highly developed and in the process of creating new ways for people to live together. The U.S.A. could be part of it; however, they are still struggling tremendously because of great differences in values within the population.

The Canadian way of life and the Scandinavian way of life are probably the most advanced indications of a new direction. Even if Scandinavia is leading and marrying modern industrial development with living in tune with the environment at a far advanced level, Canada has all the attributes it would take to catch up. Because of Canada's richness in land and resources and its unique composition of many different cultures, the dynamics are in our favour.

The Economy at a Turning Point

We are living in a fast-changing world. When I was involved in a think-tank in Berlin in the early and mid eighties, we arrived at the conclusion that the Soviet Union could not be sustained. When I shared this vision with friends outside the think-tank, they would laugh and say the Soviet Empire was so strong, led by a well established party with a military of the same size and strength as the U.S.A., that it would be very unlikely that it would not be sustainable as a structure. At the think-tank we judged that the collapse would happen by the turn of the century; ironically enough it even happened much earlier than we predicted. Starting in Hungary, Czechoslovakia, East Germany and Poland at the end of 1989, including the fall of the Berlin Wall, it did not take very long before the entire Soviet Empire collapsed.

People would say it was Gorbachev and his "Perestroika" revolutionary reform thinking that triggered all of this. Even if this

24

were correct, I would say it was primarily the communist system that ceased to be able to control the economy and manipulate the people. Gorbachev was merely the tool. Because he was honest enough to see and understand the writing on the wall, he acted in a responsible way that prevented as much damage as possible.

You don't need to be part of a think-tank to detect that the American economic system also has its challenges. The gap between rich and poor is widening further, and it is difficult to assess what will happen next. Militarism and consumerism will continue to use resources on a grand scale, almost as much as the rest of the world combined. Will the U.S.A. continue to be able to attract enough foreign investments to cover for the tremendous annual trade deficit? Will the present administration be able to continue in their drive to control the world? Will the stock market, which more and more has developed into some kind of gambling institution, be able to develop into something more respectable, transparent and accountable? We don't know, but chances are that "The American Dream," which for a few hundred years attracted millions of immigrants, will also need to be "re-dreamed" and adjusted to the reality of today's life in the U.S.A. The outcome will of course have a tremendous impact on development in Canada. However, the sooner we intensify our "Canadian way of life," the sooner we will gain our independence and find our own success.

All it will take is some leadership, some intuition and a vision, and the Canadian way of life could lead the rest of the world.

Chapter Two

A Picture of Canada
Enroute to Prosperity

Historic

In an ideal world, we are all focusing on doing the right thing at the right time.

I will therefore present a scenario in which Canada is in this ideal world and we are unhindered by the many objections and the ballast of perceptions that are considered to be reality.

If we were allowed today to do all that is needed to create the type of mental, spiritual and physical prosperity we can only imagine at present, we would need a "vision" to guide us. Canada in 2020 is one such vision.

Canada 2020

Canada in 2020 will be a nation of 40 million people with a multicultural society preserving and cherishing everybody's ethnic background while at the same time embracing the gigantic opportunities of this millennium. Political will among the leaders of all parties will show the way to a Canada freed of the chains of our perceptions and inspired by the many opportunities ahead of us.

Federal-Provincial Policy on Education

Education will still be under provincial jurisdiction, but there will be a national Ministry of Education, which will be responsible for national policies and standards, including post-secondary education and training.

Former Ontario Premier, the Honourable Bob Rae, delivered his innovative review of post-secondary education in Ontario in January 2005.

Dalton McGuinty's government, under the leadership of the Honourable Mary Anne V. Chambers, Minister of Training Colleges and Universities, and the Honourable Gerard Kennedy, Minister of Education, together reformulated the education and post-secondary education strategy for Ontario in record time before the end of 2005.

The needed changes in education were introduced. They created an historic moment of re-direction, which was just as significant as the foundation of the Ontario College System under the Honourable Bill Davis in the late sixties.

There will therefore be an emphasis on creating pathways according to the talents and abilities of the students and to the requirements of the labour market. There will be a multitude of directions for students, which will start as early as grade six. This will enable the students to get some credits for their future careers. There will be less time wasted and they will be ready for the labour market at an earlier age. Programs like the Ontario Youth Apprenticeship Program (OYAP) will be standard and include most professions, and in this way will introduce knowledge in a practical and meaningful way.

Fitness, physical education, diet, well-being and lifestyle will play a much larger role, starting at pre-birth and early childhood education. Programs in these areas will be as important as in academic and skills areas.

Transfers between the various forms of school, secondary schools and post-secondary colleges and universities will be structured by federal and provincial rules, which also will be ratified on an international level between countries or blocs by UN regulations.

Skills Training

Skills training will continue to be integrated in the provincial ministries of training colleges and universities. However there will be a much stronger focus on skills training and apprenticeships, including innovative apprenticeship programs embedded in a co-op diploma program. All of these areas, including some of the other post-secondary pathways, will be started at the school level and get full credit. Funding for university programs, college programs at the diploma and degree level, and college or other skills training, including the apprenticeship/co-op diploma program, will have shifted according to society's needs. There will be an ongoing need to upgrade skills and expertise. Every credit received will be accepted as a building block and receive recognition. The public funding will grow dramatically for skills training, which will be the big winner.

Language

The language barriers and discrepancies of the young Canada will be left behind. There will be one national language. Ethnic groups will be encouraged to maintain their own culture and language. The school system and post-secondary education will in their program structures consider this, and even if the curriculum on a national level has mutual standards, the richness of each group and each area will be allowed to be embedded in it.

Even though there will be a national language, each province, and possibly strong groups within provinces, will be given the liberty to have a strong emphasis on their own language.

Health Care: Prevention a Great Success

Health care will have shifted the emphasis towards prevention.

In order to succeed with this new mandate, the national Ministry of Health will work closely together with the Ministry of Education. There will be strong support to prepare young parents for family planning and child rearing, focusing especially on the early years, which will ensure that children grow up healthier and happier than before.

Even if health care still has a tremendous clientele of people who because of their past unhealthy lifestyle place an increasing demand on the system, a shift in attitude, behaviour and lifestyle of a large group of the population will fairly quickly trigger a reversal of the situation.

It will soon start to relieve the public spending on health care. With every year of prevention there will be a corresponding increase in well-being and reduction in health care costs. My paper "Canada Eat and Live Smart," included in this book, shows that the benefits and change in lifestyle and the subsequent annual reduction of one percent of the cost per year will soon lead to a tremendous improvement in health and well-being.

Furthermore, it will in the very few years from 2005 to 2015 have led to savings of hundreds of billions of dollars, which will be available for education and industrial innovation.

The Wellness Movement as a Dynamic Economic Vehicle

The wellness movement, which has developed quietly below the surface for many years, is now slowly taking on a dimension that will dramatically change our world. I want to claim it will change for the better. The wellness growth will have two main dimensions, one focused on the actual improvement of our well being and the other directed towards economical opportunities.

Already today this segment of the economy in North America represents more than $220 billion of business, or roughly one sixth of our food consumption of $1.2 trillion, or one eight of the present $1.7 trillion drug sales. This is a stunning figure, but when we consider that drugs long ago surpassed food in sales, it is more understandable.

The 90 million North American baby boomers born in the period after World War II and before the early 1960s are giving a major boost to development. The older and more financially affluent and independent members of this group are becoming more and more wellness oriented and willing to invest substantially into their well-being, fitness and health. In Canada, we are talking about slightly less than 10 million baby boomers and more than $20 billion of business.

At a first glance this seems very high, but when we look at the many segments of this industry we can clearly see that we are just at the beginning.

Some segments of the health food industry:

- Vitamins

- Health foods

- Weight-loss products

- Nutritional supplements

- Fitness clubs

- Spas

- Fitness tourism

- Health-food restaurants

- Preventive medicine

- Wellness drugs for sexual drive, improved skin, etc.

- Cosmetic surgery

- And many more

The wish to stay healthy and fit, to be able to enjoy life in an active way, and the strong desire to stay young are all leading to a big shift in thinking.

In the past, retired people accepted their rapidly declining health and fitness. But the change in awareness, the easy access to information, and the many more examples of fit and healthy seniors create a dramatic demand for better and healthier products and services. Therefore the wellness industry will be a large part of the "industrial innovation" discussed in the next paragraph. If you are interested in more details of this remarkable development, I would recommend the book *The Wellness Revolution: How to*

Make a Fortune in the Trillion Dollar Industry (Paul Zane Pilzer, published by Wiley, John Wiley and Sons, Inc.).

Industrial Innovation

Because Canadian political leaders at the beginning of this century led Canada in an innovative direction, in 2015 Canada will have caught up and be among the five leading countries in innovation and productivity. How will this come about?

Canada will embrace the kind of opportunities talked about in this book. A true renaissance will be created with aggressively forward-looking education, health care and investment strategy. Canada will be an innovative society leading the world in a new direction.

Research, Applied Research and Commercialization

This whole area will benefit greatly by the establishment of an "Agency for Innovation and Job Creation." The huge amounts of capital that were primarily flowing into pure university research will be increased drastically but for a more pragmatic and regulated use, requiring research to be tied to applied research and commercialization.

Medium- and small-size companies will have similar opportunities as big corporations have, and universities and colleges will be on even terms to draw funding for their individual or joint research and development work.

This area will equally benefit from the reduction in health care costs once prevention starts to bring the turnaround, and the overall climate of innovation and job creation will direct funding to the areas where there is a need. Access will be easier and less bureaucratic but guided by strict rules of transparent accountability.

This turnaround will catapult Canada from being a world leader in research to becoming a world leader in innovative research, applied research and commercialization.

Innovative energy sources, transport systems, water conservation and waste-water management will be some of the cornerstones of the Canadian 2015 success story.

Fortunately, Paul Martin's minority government, which started in the middle of 2004, will lead to a complete change in attitude within the House of Commons. Instead of continuing the never-ending fights within the parties, they will create an innovative strategy that will allow the opposition to contribute in a constructive way. Partnerships with the various parties will be formed according to the subject. A lot of new policies, regulations and laws will be created and passed with overwhelming support from all parties, both in parliament and in the senate.

The real breakthrough will come because the government in 2005 will create an "Agency for Innovation and Job Creation." This agency will work directly within the prime minister's office and will take a refreshing new approach. The prime minister will engage the leaders from all parties to participate in the creation of this agency, and each party will appoint its share of members on the agency's board according to the ratio of seats in parliament. The parties will agree to appoint non-partisan professionals as external members of the board and one representative from each of the eleven involved ministries and the prime minister's office. Furthermore, there will be one representative from each opposition party (three) and an independent president and CEO who also will be the ex officio member as board secretary (appointed by the Prime Minister). The outcome will be that a board, consisting of twenty-five top professionals from all spheres of society, will be able to create an independent vision and dynamic.

Board Structure of the "Agency of Innovation and Job Creation"

Membership:

10 non-partisan professionals appointed by all parties according to their ratio of seats in the parliament

1 appointed by the Prime Minister

1 appointed by the Minister of Finance

1 appointed by the Minister of Education and Training

1 appointed by the Minister of Health

1 appointed by the Minister of Industry

1 appointed by the Minister of Natural Resources/Energy

1 appointed by the Minister of the Environment

1 appointed by the Minister of Infrastructure/Public Works

1 appointed by the Minister of Transportation

1 appointed by the Minister of Immigration and Human Resources

1 appointed by the Minister of Agriculture

3 appointed as representatives of the three opposition parties

1 Independent President and CEO appointed by the Prime Minister as Secretary of the Board

25 Total

This board will elect its own chair and vice-chair with membership limited to two terms of three years.

Canada as World Leader in Renewable Energy

Soon after the installation of the "Agency of Innovation and Job Creation," the federal government, together with the provincial governments, will develop a national policy on energy.

This very entrepreneurial policy will allow, without further hurdles, the brisk introduction of a Canadian Standard for Energy. Once the national policy and standards are introduced, there will not be any more interference. There will be speedy development of most renewable energy resources.

Subsidies will be eliminated as it becomes apparent that the high environmental standards for all energies make subsidies obsolete. This will quickly enable most of the alternative clean energies to compete. Once the high standards on emissions are in place, coal and gas will become more expensive than wind or solar energy. The drastic reduction of production costs for solar photo voltaic panels (PV) will contribute to this. Between 2007 and 2010, the cost for one PV unit will gradually fall below one dollar, putting solar power energy generation through PV on even footing with traditional powers and wind power for the first time. Solar power will create tremendous additional commercial opportunities when the installation of independent systems for household and commercial use becomes popular and even the standard for any new construction.

Another breakthrough in fuel-cell technology will enable a conversion of solar power or wind power into stored power and in this way eliminate the handicap of power production interruption caused by periods without sun or wind.

Because Canada creates more than 50 percent of its energy out of hydro and because of many additional evolving opportunities in biomass, geothermal, wave energy and landfill gas, Canada will in 2020 become the first nation on Earth to generate all its electricity out of renewable resources. The annual OECD published ranking will for the first time show Canada at the top and will include an analysis of what triggered Canada's stunning success. It will be obvious that the shift to conservation and sustainable energy will have created an enormous boost to the economy and inspired an innovative investment climate. The analysis will also indicate that by focusing on improving lifestyle and introducing preventative holistic health care in conjunction with an inclusive education and training agenda, Canada's tremendous potential will be fully utilized.

Innovative transportation systems and lightweight, low consumption, electric and fuel-cell-driven cars designed and built in Canada will have a great impact. Because of the high cost and/or risk, oil, gas and atomic energies will all be phased out of electricity production between 2010 and 2020.

Innovative Rail, Road and Transport Systems Will Help Canada to Overcome the Great Distances

The opening of the "Agency of Innovation and Job Creation" in 2005 and its overarching mandate and power will create the ability to launch high-profile policies and programs among ministries and parties without the normal lengthy bureaucratic and parliamentarian hurdles.

Due to our nation's size and low population density except for a few exploding urban areas, transportation and communication play a much more significant role than in most other countries. As at Canada's beginning as a nation at the end of the 19th century, when first the steam train and ships and later the automobile opened up our huge country, the innovation strategy will open new horizons within public and private transportation. To link rural and urban areas and to develop more efficient and reliable means of transportation, the new agency will early on put a focus on overcoming the particular challenges of densely populated urban areas.

Having sufficient electrical energy available, a plan will be developed to install a magnetic monorail system linking all major centres and subsystems of regional and local magnetic monorails and conventional electrical systems within the country and within urban areas. Canadian and overseas companies and entrepreneurs will improve and convert the traditional two-rail system to electricity and redesign the new magnetic monorail system to fit the Canadian climate and conditions. The already existing rail manufacturing industry will go into joint ventures for the manufacturing of these innovate systems. The expansion will create hundreds of thousands of new jobs. It will be possible to install a first net of magnetic monorail trains along the main Trans-Canada Highway corridors from coast to coast before 2015. It will be relatively easy to use the middle section of the Trans-Canada Highway as the ideal, readily available space for a two-way track. The same middle section, which for 80 percent of the Trans-Canada runs from east to west, can ideally be used to install south-facing solar voltaic panels, utilizing the same space to produce huge quantities of electricity. The first corridor, between Windsor, Ontario, and Quebec City, will be opened by 2010. The Metro Toronto downtown area and Toronto Airport will be linked to this corridor at the same time. This will bring a tremendous relief to the public transit system in the GTA.

Imagine that the non-stop trip from Toronto to Montreal takes less than one and a half hours. Even station stops can be done without a big time loss, because it only takes three minutes, or nine kilometres, to get back up to 430 kilometres per hour. The very successful Transrapid started its operation between Shanghai Long Yang Station and Pudong International Airport on December 31, 2003, and as of July 3, 2004, had already transported more than one million passengers. The thirty-kilometre track is travelled at a regular service speed of 430 kilometres per hour and has achieved the world record for top speed for commercial trains of 501 kilometres per hour. The distance between Toronto Airport and Union station will be travelled in less than six minutes.

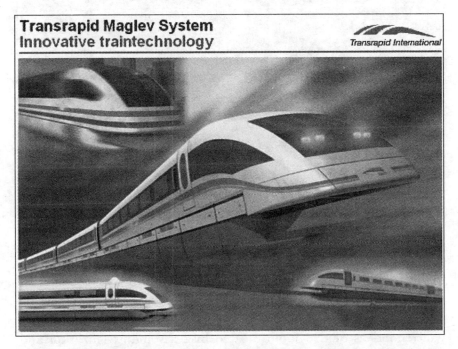

Transrapid Maglev System
Innovative traintechnology

Transrapid International

The Superspeed Transrapid Maglev system has neither wheels nor axles nor gearing. It does not drive—it hovers without touching the guideway, with no friction or wear. Electronics replace mechanical parts. The function of wheel-on-rail—i.e., support and guidance, propulsion and braking—are taken over by an electromagnetic levitation and propulsion system. Transrapid works contact-free. Heavy snowfall in the winter initially created some challenges for this system, but changes in the design of the monorail makes it much easier to keep the tracks free of snow and ice than with a traditional rail system.

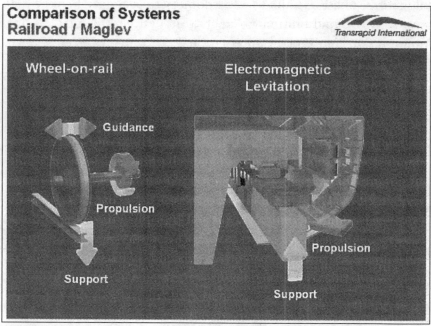

**Comparison of Systems
Railroad / Maglev**

Transrapid International

Wheel-on-rail

Electromagnetic Levitation

Guidance

Propulsion

Support

Propulsion

Support

(Detailed material is available on the Transrapid Web page, www.transrapid.de. Go to "Presentation," which shows technical details and worldwide installation. The U.S.A. Web page, www.transrapid-usa.com, informs about the numerous successful installations in the U.S.A.)

This thirty-year-old, proven, innovative and yet simple technology will propel Canada to become the most transport efficient country in the world within less than two decades. The boost to the Canadian economy will be of such a magnitude that Canada will become the preferred place for international investments. The economic dynamic will remind us of the boom created by early industrialization and linking the country by train in the nineteenth century.

Shipping on the Water Is Still a Viable Option

Because of the convenience of the automobile and the airplane, North American society has to a large extent forgotten that there still are many train corridors and shipping routes available as a very viable option to move goods and passengers at a much better rate and with much less pollution. As the picture below indicates, a single middle-sized freighter can carry the load of 870 trucks. A single traditional freight train can handle up to a few hundred truckloads.

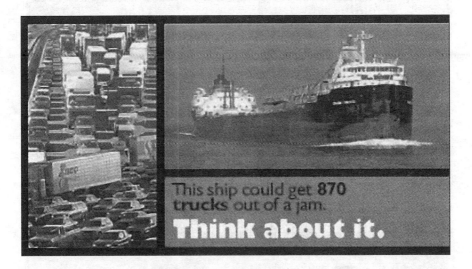

This ship could get **870** trucks out of a jam.

Think about it.

To relieve our congested highway system, it is time that we consider using this type of shipping to a much larger extent. Combined with the envisioned innovative "Transrapid" system (primarily for passengers), it could easily relieve our highways by up to 50 percent and this way undo *disastrous* traffic congestion, particularly in all urban areas.

The Great Lakes and St. Lawrence Seaway System has a high-quality infrastructure that easily can handle a doubling of the traffic without the need of investing one single penny. Last year 41 million tons were shipped *through the St. Lawrence Seaway*, but the capacity is between 80 and 100 million tons (www.hwyh20.com). By increasing the volume the cost could even be reduced and the turnaround time and schedules could be improved drastically. The environmental impact would be very positive. When we look at the comparative index that follows, we can see how favourable marine or rail transportation is .

Comparative Index	Marine	Rail	Truck
Energy Consumption	1	2.2	9.7
Emissions Output	1	1.4	7.6
Accidents	1	13.7	74.7
Spills	1	10.0	37.5
Noise	1	1.4	1.3

(See http://www.st-laurent.org for details.)

In Central European countries like the Benelux (Netherlands, Belgium and Luxembourg) and Germany, inland shipping by boat has over the years increased dramatically and is many times the size of the North American volume. The volume of goods and passengers shipped by train in all European countries is more than fifty times bigger.

Industrial Innovation in Combination with the Overall Renewal Makes Canada World Leader in Productivity and Innovation

An innovative and economic dynamic business climate will create synergies that lead to the establishment of many additional activities. It will also attract a massive influx of entrepreneurial and creative people. Dr. Richard Florida's book *The Rise of the Creative*

Class indicates what will be needed for Canada to attract the doers, makers and shakers. It is very interesting to learn about the shift from a traditional agricultural society to a traditional industrial society, followed by a takeover by the creative society that today represents more than 30 percent of the population.

Canada will not only attract the creative class from countries around the globe; it will also mobilize the tremendous potential in the people from within.

Lightweight Electrical Cars

Under these circumstances it will not take long for Canada's car and car parts manufacturing industry to venture into new directions. The tremendously efficient public transport system soon will encourage travellers to use their own vehicles only when needed for short distances outside the public system. This will create the need for small, light cars low in consumption and easy to park. Even if people in the less developed countryside keep a market for SUVs going, these cars will change dramatically into elegant, lightweight hybrids powered by electricity, ethanol and fuel cells, etc.

With all the technology evolving out of the renewable energy sector matched with diverse expertise, particularly in car-parts production, a new dimension in lightweight cars with various alternative engines will be developed, including fuel cell technology. They will be successfully launched on the North American home market and soon also on the world market, where in spite of tough competition they will conquer interesting market shares.

Mini lightweight-car rental depots at airports, train stations and bus stations, with hassle-free self-service and immediate, around-the-clock access, will reduce the number of private cars and create a very flexible and mobile society with pollution-free trains and cars.

Because of the efficient public overland transport, air transportation will be reduced and used only for long-distance travel, beyond a thousand kilometres. The airports will be converted to combined air, bus and train stations, and the space that will be freed because of the huge reduction in flights may be converted into distributions centres for products that are going to be moved in standardized containers from planes to trains or trucks. A large part of the transportation of goods within the populated areas will move away from the traditional trucking system to a highly efficient lightweight container system, which will move around the country on computer controlled trains. In case of rural or ocean destinations the same container system will be integrated into traditional rail, trucking and ocean and seaway shipping systems all based on one universal module.

Various standardized modules will mean a very flexible shipping and transportation system. Three of the smallest modules will fit into a twenty-foot ocean container (six in a forty-foot unit). Two of the middle-size modules will fit into a twenty-foot container and four into a forty-foot unit. The next size will be a twenty-foot unit, which will be a modernized version of the twenty-foot ocean container. The same technique will be applied to the twenty-foot container.

With this system, shipping on a national level will be fully automated and computer steered, allowing the modules to travel from place of shipping to destination without being touched by human hands, at a speed that enables trans-Canada transfers of module-sized goods within less than two days, at a cost lower than conventional trucking.

Environmental Strategies

At first it will require a great effort and huge investment to move away from environmentally unfriendly technologies developed during the nineteenth and twentieth centuries. But the savings of energy, the gain in efficiency and in comfort, soon will make society take the new way of life for granted. Environmental strategies focused on creating clean air and clean water will present unlimited opportunities for creative industrial development and user-friendly energy-efficient homes and buildings.

The development of renewable energy as the main source of electricity, the new means of transport, much better designed homes and buildings with excellent insulation and design, much improved water and waste-water management and organic farming, all by themselves without too many additional measures, will turn things around. The environment will almost instantly change for the better through the immense improvements after generations of abuse. Real forest management can be implemented, and a ban on most pesticides will start to show its first positive effects.

The Canada Mortgage and Housing Corporation, which early on promoted energy-efficient houses, will together with industry and architects develop house-building systems that are easy to assemble and to integrate in any part of Canada, utilizing the sun and other components like earth pumps to make the houses self-sufficient and low in water consumption (see innovative ideas at www.cmhc.ca). There are already many energy-efficient homes, small and large, on the market. One owner of a big, self-sufficient home has created a Web page, www.solarhouse.com, and is willing to share his experience.

Because of the much more holistic approach in all areas of life, nature will automatically be much less burdened, and the environmental rules and strategies will be accepted as sensible regulations and happily followed by most people.

Conserving Water and Waste-Water Management

Canada has between 25 and 30 percent of the freshwater of the world. Yet the industrialization, intensive farming, urbanization and pollution will put such a dramatic burden on Canadian drinking water that many bodies of water will lose their natural balance and become sour, over nourished or dead. This will result in an ironic situation that will make it necessary to chlorinate drinking water even more in most of Canada. Because of a lack of properly trained people or quality equipment, many places chlorinate heavily just to make sure that nobody will get an infection. We should consider that chlorine is a very dangerous poison and over-chlorinating water will affect people's health and ultimately add another burden on Mother Nature. Because of this, billions of bottles of water are being produced annually. Various factors like production and transport create another burden on the environment. It really was, and is, a vicious circle. It would have been better to keep a clean supply of water in the first place.

With a focus on conserving energy, water and all of our resources, the Canadian Renewal will create new, better and less wasteful ways. Drinking water will be treated as a treasured resource that is not wasted through leaking pipes or wasteful toilets, etc. The huge quantities of fresh water used in farming, manufacturing and for moving waste water out of homes will be reduced drastically through improved methods with much less loss. The overall environmentally-friendly behaviour will also have a large impact on water levels and quality.

Around 2015, for the first time in more than a hundred years, the water quality will in a natural way dramatically improve. It will be standard to separate drinking and household water from wastewater use and, because of excellent economical filters and reverse osmosis systems that will be standard in every home, drinking water will again be of very good quality. Water used for washing will be regenerated by mini filters, reverse osmosis or organic septic systems and utilized for toilet flushing or similar things. Biodegradable detergent, soaps and cleaners will be standard. Many new developments in sewage processing or utilization in form of mini bio reactors in homes and commercial buildings will help immensely and create an additional industrial boom, which will add to the prosperity of Canadian society.

Innovative vacuum toilet systems hardly use any water; the dryer sewage will, together with any other organic waste, be utilized and through a bio reactor converted into energy or compost, and the separated clean water will be recirculated for toilet flushing.

Lakes and rivers that were polluted will gradually regain their balance. The fish stocks will revive, and swimming in these waters will be safe again.

New Canadian Organic Agriculture Beats Traditional Methods

The gradual changeover to organic farming will bring a revival of smaller farm units across the country. These farms will again be economical and competitive, because of technical improvements but foremost because of a big shift in supply and demand all across North America and even across the world. Just like in Canada, the demand for organic produce, fruit and grain will increase dramatically in the U.S.A. as well as in the rest of the world. Therefore more and more consumers demand home-grown products from their direct neighbourhood. Once the small farm units show a financial viability, a lot of former farmers or descendents of farmers will move back to the countryside. This will also be encouraged by the much-improved transportation and communication systems that will link people to the cities in a comfortable way.

During the winter months, farmers can concentrate their production in hothouses, fuelled by a combination of solar, wind, ground pumps, bio mass and fuel cell technology. Canadian farming will attract a lot of city people and a lot of private people, including retirees who are starting small efficient greenhouses in conjunction with their energy-self-sufficient homes. Their produce is either for home consumption, for sale on a small local scale or for free distribution among friends and relatives.

Wellness as a Big Part of the Industrial Innovation

Many of the changes I have dealt with in the Canada 2020 Vision will automatically improve peoples' well-being and quality of life. At the same time there will be an increased demand on wellness services and products that will lead to the strong expansion of the whole wellness industry.

The stronger focus on prevention will at the same time create a stronger desire to further improve health and well-being. The medical profession so accustomed to dealing only with fixing sickness will quickly adapt to the changes and begin to fully endorse and become part of the modern preventative and wellness society.

The boost to the Canadian wellness industry in combination with the overall innovative initiatives in all fields will give the long awaited spiritual and economical renewal Canadians are longing for.

Revised Immigration Policy Helps Canada's Prosperity

When the "Innovation and Job Creation" agency starts its work in 2005, one of its first tasks will be to create inner-ministerial co-operation between HRSD, Immigration, Industry Canada and the Ministry of Education and Training. Together they will create a flexible federal system in conjunction with their provincial counter-parts. This flexible immigration policy will be applied to the actual needs on the labour market and adjusted continuously, just like in the old days.

This flexibility combined with the extraordinary industrious and prosperous climate in Canada will attract a lot of ambitious young people from around the world, including trades people and high-calibre entrepreneurs and investors. Because of this, Canada's growth will be supported and capital will be available in abundance. It will further create hundreds of thousands of new jobs and reduce unemployment to the point that huge amounts of money out of the unemployment insurance funds and reserves will be available for the capital market. The impact will also reverse the situation for the pension plans that before were starting to suffer badly from a decline of younger people and will also avoid an otherwise pre-dicted necessary bailout of most of the pension funds.

Canadian Way of Life—A Quality Way of Life with New Economic Values

Around 2008, new policies and income tax rules around wealth building, pension plans and co-ownership in private and public com-panies will be put in place. They will encourage companies to recruit their employees as shareholders with favourable conditions for both sides. It will be mandatory that compensation received out of this be reinvested into the company towards growth or stability. Companies with an employee shareholding of more than 50 percent will receive tax preferential treatment that further helps the company to prosper. Again, the compensation will have to be applied for growth and wealth building of the corporation and its shareholders.

In 2020 Canada will be a vibrant country with a thriving economy full of optimism and endorsing a model of co-operation between governments at all levels, employers, management and employees. Just as in management, the unions will have changed their position and their approach to a joint position, full of support for each other's needs.

Because of a thriving economy and a lean public service, the public sector will benefit dramatically. Particularly, the change in health care to prevention and the following drastic reduction in health care costs will free capital that will allow education, post-secondary education and training to be funded properly. And there will be sufficient government funding available for infrastructure of any kind.

Many companies will have their employees as majority share-holders and union representatives actually change to become share-holder representatives. This new scenario will over time influence other world markets, in Europe, Asia, Australia, New Zealand, Africa and U.S.A. More and more countries will switch to the Canadian model of modern socio-capital sharing, and most public companies, even in markets outside the countries that endorse this model, will align themselves with the new thinking.

The U.S.A. will initially struggle with this model. However, after several states move successfully in this direction, the Canadian way of life will become more and more the U.S.A. way of life. This will evolve over many years and slowly but drastically change people's behaviour.

Because of employees' lifelong shareholdings in "their" com-panies, the stock exchanges and market's importance will also shift to be more of a registration place and less a place of specu-lation. The markets will still be flowing freely; however, the majority of the shares will be in the hands of loyal share-holders/employees, who are not inclined to gamble with their holdings. This automatically makes the movements of the markets much more smooth and controlled.

The scenario I have created may be considered wishful thinking by some people, too ambitious by others, and not radical enough by still others. I am convinced it could be a possible picture of our future if our politicians will show leadership and vision. We have come out of the Stone Age; the oil age is coming to an end and it is up to us to determine which way we are going next. Why not endorse a Canadian direction that will allow us to dream our own destiny and create a legacy we proudly can leave behind for our children.

Chapter Three

What are Canada's Greatest Challenges and Opportunities?

Keeping a Public Health Service Viable by Directing the Focus to Prevention: Health Reform—and How We Can Bury Canadians' Most "Sacred Cow" Without Sacrificing Canadian Values

The present Canadian health service model with its ever-escalating cost is not sustainable. People need to take ownership of their health and well-being again and be encouraged to make conscious choices for a healthy lifestyle.

Some time before the Romanow Report was finalized and published in 2002, I led a brief but quite conclusive study on our Canadian health system at St. Lawrence College. A copy of this study was shared with Mr. Romanow and our political leaders. It was very disappointing to learn that his $16 million study found only a dramatic need for better communication and co-operation between the provinces and the federal government and drastic increases in federal and provincial funding to keep the system afloat. There is not one single innovative proposal for launching a campaign on prevention or change in people's behaviour and lifestyle in the report. What a waste of effort and resources. If that

$16 million had been used for an awareness campaign for a better lifestyle as proposed in the SLC report, we would already be well on our way to improving health.

At the same time I also hand-delivered my study, which I originally called "Ontario Eat and Live Smart," to the Ontario Mike Harris government through the Chair of the Cabinet, the Honourable Bob Runciman. I chose this route because of the good relationship I had developed with him as our local MPP in Brockville. It had proven quite successful two years before when a study I conducted on apprenticeships with Bob Runciman's support actually did get a long overdue $88 million new apprenticeship funding for the Ontario College System (I will report on this under the skills/education agenda).

I recall clearly how excited Bob Runciman was about the SLC health system study and that he indicated that he would try to champion this in a similar fashion. I do not doubt Mr. Runciman's good intentions to also champion this cause, but it soon became clear that the change from Mike Harris as Premier of Ontario to Ernie Eves left the province in a state that made innovative changes more unlikely.

Having failed to start the implementation of "Ontario Eat and Live Smart," I renamed it "Canada Eat and Live Smart." The renamed report was at a later date, in April 2003, presented to the Right Honourable Paul Martin and, at around the same time, to people like the then Ontario opposition critic on education (present Minister of Education) Gerard Kennedy and a little later to the then opposition leader (present Premier of Ontario) Dalton McGuinty.

April 28, 2003

The Hon. Paul Martin, M.P. LaSalle-Emard
Room 458 Confederation Building
House of Commons
Ottawa, ON
K1A 0A6

"Canada Eat and Live Smart"

Dear Mr. Martin:

I'm pleased to present you with an innovative proposal that would address the serious problem of increasing demand on health services as a result of a growing need to treat degenerative and chronic illnesses, many of which are directly related to lifestyle and diet. Done right, this proposed campaign will not create additional cost but relieve the system and start a turnaround with potential cost savings in the billions of dollars.

In Canada, we have one of the best health care systems in the world. But here, as elsewhere, the cost of health care is increasing at such an alarming rate that many now believe our publicly financed system is "unsustainable."

The challenge, therefore, is to find ways to control costs while promoting people to be healthy and productive.

There is increasing evidence of a link between illness, poor diets and a sedentary lifestyle. An unhealthy lifestyle—especially during pregnancy, early childhood and among young people—escalates health care costs, reduces productivity and threatens our ability as a society to remain competitive.

I'm proposing a campaign in which the Government of Canada takes a leadership role in developing a series of unique incentives and programs in partnership with its many funding partners and the private sector and acts as a model for other jurisdictions.

What leadership did to combat smoking and its high cost to society, leadership can do to promote a healthier lifestyle and its many benefits to our society. Opportunities now exist in preventive and holistic approaches, and I believe we should take advantage of these practical solutions to some of the challenges facing us.

"Canada Eat and Live Smart" is a proposal that will lead to better health and well-being and conserve valuable public resources needed for such areas as education, the environment and economic development.

St. Lawrence College is dedicated to playing a responsible and leading role in helping to make this change happen. The proposal, which I am forwarding to you, outlines some of the ways we believe we can be helpful.

The Romanow report identified the present needs, but it missed seeing the opportunities that could make Canada a world leader in innovation and health.

We are most anxious to see this attached proposal go ahead, and I would welcome the opportunity to discuss it with you or other members of your platform.

It will take real leadership to move this exciting vision forward. I do not doubt for a minute that you, if you want to, could make this agenda for the future a reality, and I would of course be willing to help to get this initiative off the ground and make it a success for your government.

I look forward to learning your reaction to these proposals and how we can advance them through the bureaucratic and political process.

With my best regards,

Volker Thomsen
President and CEO
St. Lawrence College

"CANADA EAT AND LIVE SMART"
A Program to Improve Canadians' Health and Conserve Resources

The Challenges

All across Canada, governments and the private sector are struggling to curb ever-increasing health care costs.

The Canadian Institute for Health Information says total health care spending in Canada—mostly by the public sector—reached the $100 billion mark in 2001. In Ontario, 46 cents out of every provincial tax dollar now go to health care, severely limiting funds available for other vital public services. The cost of health care is increasing at such an alarming rate that many now believe our publicly financed system is "unsustainable." Such major factors as an aging population and costly new drugs and medical procedures mean that ways of curbing costs must be found.

An unhealthy lifestyle—especially during pregnancy and early childhood and among young people—causes major health problems, escalates health care costs, reduces productivity and threatens our competitiveness.

There is increasing evidence of a link between illness and both poor diets and a sedentary lifestyle. The concern is especially pronounced as it relates to embryos, babies, children and youth.

For example:

• The Early Years Study co-chaired by Margaret McCain and Fraser Mustard (1999) clearly shows the relationship between early brain and child development and learning, behaviour and health throughout all stages of life.

• Heart disease and strokes remains the number one killer in Canada, claiming 79,000 lives this year, according to the Heart and Stroke Foundation of Canada.

• Obesity, a known risk factor for heart disease and stroke, has been called an "epidemic" by some health care experts. Statistics Canada estimates 46 percent of all adult Canadians are overweight or obese and current trends indicate this number will increase. Almost one in four (23 percent) of children age 7 to 12 are obese.

• In the U.S., the Surgeon General estimates that the total costs attributed to overweight and obesity amount to $ 117 billion in the year 2000 in a country where obesity among adults has doubled since 1980 and the prevalence among adolescents has tripled in the past two decades. Type 2 diabetes has shown a sharp rise among children and adolescents. Over 80 percent of Americans with diabetes are overweight or obese, according to the same Dec. 2001 report.

• The number of Canadians age 12 and over who have diabetes is estimated at 1.4 million. The prevalence rate among aboriginals is triple that of the general population.

• While 70 percent of Canadians know that eating fruits and vegetables can prevent cancer, heart disease and stroke, only 36 percent consume the Health Canada Food Guide recommended daily servings of these products (A. C. Nielsen study, July 2001).

- Studies increasingly show that physical activity is as essential to good health as a balanced diet and avoiding tobacco (Health Canada, March 2001). The Canadian Medical Association Journal estimates that about $2.1 billion of the total direct health costs in Canada were attributable to such inactivity in 1999 and a 10 percent reduction in the prevalence of physical inactivity has the potential to reduce costs by $ 210 million a year.

As consumer interest in healthy living increases, there is a corresponding increase in public concern related to health and safety regulation issues in the food and agriculture industries.

The growing popularity and availability of organic foods and the increased interest in fitness is testimony to the desire by many to stay healthy. (Agriculture Canada predicts the domestic organic industry will grow at an average 20 percent a year to become a $3.1 billion industry by 2005.)

As well, a major demand has developed for herbal medicines, dietary supplements and other forms of holistic health care, as evidenced in the spread of so-called health food outlets and the increased availability of these products in grocery and drug stores. However, consumers often lack the knowledge to differentiate between the ways various food products are produced and processed and their impact on healthy eating. Information is often conflicting or confusing.

In addition, high profile issues such as tainted blood supplies, mad cow disease and contaminated water have raised many questions about the role of both the public and private sectors in ensuring public safety.

Modern methods of food production have given rise to concerns over the effects of insecticides and pesticides and genetically engineered products. Concern over chemical use is evidenced at the community level, where 37 municipalities across the country have banned the cosmetic use of pesticides in response to scientific studies indicating they are a potential threat to human health, especially for children. The Government of Canada has recently introduced legislation that responds to this trend.

As well, the public's heavy reliance on meat as a major component of North American diets is creating for all governments new public policy issues, such as the amount of natural resources required in the production process and environmental and health concerns linked to so-called "factory farms."

The Opportunities

In Canada, governments have regarded health promotion as part of their mandate for the past 25 years as it is widely accepted that to protect and improve health, preventive efforts have to go beyond education and the clinic. Government's role has long been established in using social marketing techniques of persuasion to modify behaviour. There is no better example of this than anti-smoking campaigns.

Twenty years ago, it would have been considered impossible to seriously change long-held attitudes and customs related to smoking and their impact on health. Today, Canada leads the world in the success and commitment of its various anti-smoking efforts, which have reduced *disease and premature death, health care costs and lost productivity.*

The same opportunity now exists to take a lead role in discouraging unhealthy diets and lifestyles and promoting changes that will make children and adults healthier and happier while reducing health care costs and conserving resources.

This can be done through a high profile program that brings together leaders who are visionaries, conducts and coordinates research, trains early-childhood teachers, other teachers and health care workers about the benefits of good nutrition and exercise, develops sponsorship and marketing programs with the private sector and spearheads reliable, effective public education programs.

The program is focused on the belief that there is more to health than health care.

From a financial perspective, the benefits are awesome:

This year, the Canadian government will spend approximately $100 billion on health care (www.hc-sc.gc.ca/english/can/spending). Just saving one percent per year *represents* conserving some *$1 billion* annually—money badly needed for such other areas as education, the environment and economic development.

Ideally, we must plan a future in which *over a 10-year period* the level of health is improved so that we actually save at least 10 percent. Using today's figures, this represents a $10 billion saving per year by the end of the decade.

This is a far cry from some forecasts, which suggest that if we continue at our current rate of increase, our health budget will go up by 20 percent over the next 10 years. Therefore, a real 10 percent decrease would actually represent a difference in saving of 30 percent or about $30 billion for the period or 3 billion per year. These are the direct costs. However, if productivity loss and other factors are included, the difference can easily be quadrupled and total a 10 year contribution of about $120 billion for government, business and communities.

How this can be accomplished

It will be argued that changing lifestyles is a difficult task. However, the long-range awareness campaign around the harmful effects of smoking is surely an excellent example of how an effective program can successfully modify behaviour. This

Canadian success story has saved our economy untold billions of dollars and spared millions of people from the misery of a nicotine addiction and the health problems resulting from it.

Only 25 years ago almost 50 percent of Canadian adults were smokers; the rate dropped to 31 percent in 1990 and is now just under 25 percent (www.cancer.ca, www.heartandstroke.ca). Arguably, turning smokers into non-smokers is a bigger challenge than convincing the public of the merits of eating well and exercising.

Getting Started

• Launch **"CANADA EAT AND LIVE SMART,"** a medium- to long-range campaign to improve Canadians' health and conserve resources, supported by strong political and private sector leadership.

• Establish a small, effective office consisting of highly motivated professionals (run like a company with a CEO). This office should be independent—perhaps a Quality of Life Secretariat—but report to the Prime Minister and work closely with all ministries and agencies involved (e.g. health, education, training, colleges and universities, environment, economic development, community and social services, agriculture, food and rural affairs etc.).

• Develop partnerships in both the public and private sectors.

• Develop an awareness and public information campaign.

• Offer training to early childhood educators and teachers about the impact of diet, lifestyle, exercise etc. This can be delivered, for example, through the Canadian College System. Curriculum can be made available immediately by combining existing programs and adding some material from The Canadian College of Naturopathic Medicine. For example, the training will give teachers credit under the point system recently launched by the Ontario College of Teachers.

The curriculum for early childhood education, primary school, junior high school and high-school will be altered and enriched by an entertaining and exciting program designed to appeal to young people.

Promotional materials and media will be appropriate for the various target audiences. For example, daily 5-minute skits can be prepared for airing by CBC and other broadcasters, in which a well-known personality will introduce products, basic recipes, sports and any other issues promoting a happy/healthy lifestyle. This program could also involve some well-known Canadians who have recovered from serious illnesses by changing their lifestyles and diets. Wide use would also be made of public service announcements, talk shows, print materials, public speaking opportunities, web sites and interactive materials of particular interest to young people.

The Partners

"Canada Eat and Live Smart" would require a partnership of governments and the non-profit and private sectors:

- strong political leadership to provide the catalyst for action

- government bureaucracy to promote co-operation among the various ministries and agencies involved, organize symposiums and recommend the process for administering the program—perhaps through a secretariat

- education partners (the Ministries of Education and Training, Colleges and Universities, faculties of education, community colleges, school boards, teachers, parent councils, physical education specialists, early childhood education centers) to provide institutions and staff with the knowledge and tools they need to promote the program among children and parents

- health care partners (ministry, district health councils, health units, professionals, professional associations, private companies) to develop and market programs to their staff and stakeholders (e.g. Physicians for a Healthy Lifestyle has been active on the federal level)

- foundations dedicated to helping children and families and strengthening social programs

- corporate leaders to pioneer new business opportunities and reduce/eliminate opposition from special interest groups affected by change

- agriculture and food industry members to take a leadership role in developing and promoting healthy lifestyle products and services

- high profile members of the entertainment/sports world to act as champions and role models promoting good diets and physical activity, especially among children (Canadian Olympic stars have shown a willingness to participate in health promotions. In the U.S., entertainer Bill Cosby has been used widely in public service announcements to promote healthy eating for children)

In Summary

"Canada Eat and Live Smart" provides the opportunity for the Government of Canada to show it has the vision and determination to take a stand against current unhealthy lifestyles that exact such a high toll in human suffering, health care costs and lost productivity. By establishing an office with the necessary expertise and resources to design and implement the program, the government could provide unique incentives and programs in partnership with its many funding partners and the private sector and act as a role model for other jurisdictions.

What leadership did to combat smoking and its high cost to society, leadership can do to promote a healthier lifestyle and its many benefits to our society.

NB: At St. Lawrence College, we have already identified a specific role for ourselves by applying to the Ontario College of Teachers to be designated an official supplier of both elective and core courses for teachers. This is part of the OCT's requirements for ongoing professional learning by all its registrants. Through our Kingston, Brockville and Cornwall campuses, we are proposing to offer to teachers a variety of courses, including courses on the importance of healthy lifestyles and the link between good food and exercise and good mental and physical health. Furthermore we would like to expand the "Early Childhood Education" curriculum to include some of the important aspects mentioned earlier.

We are most anxious to explore with the government additional ways in which we can be part of the **"Canada Eat and Live Smart"** program.

The author of this proposal is certainly willing to provide leadership to get this initiative off the ground and make it a success.

Volker Thomsen
President and CEO
St. Lawrence College

Copies of this report were given to most of the leading Ontario and Federal politicians: including Roy Romanow, Chair of the Royal Commission on Health Reform, Dalton McGuinty, then leader of the Ontario Opposition, and Anne McLellan, Minister of Health. Their responses are included for your information.

Commission on the
Future of Health Care
in Canada

Commission sur
l'avenir des soins de santé
au Canada

Commissioner
Roy J. Romanow, Q.C.

Executive Director
Gregory Marchildon, PhD

P.O. Box 160, Station Main
Saskatoon, Canada S7K 3K4
306 975-6888   Fax 306 975-6890
www.healthcarecommission.ca

Commissaire
Roy J. Romanow, c.r.

Directeur exécutif
Gregory Marchildon

C.P. 160, Succursale Main
Saskatoon, Canada S7K 3K4
306 975-6888   Télécopieur 306 975-6890
www.commissionsoinsdesante.ca

April 23, 2002

Volker Thomsen
President and CEO
St. Lawrence College
King and Portsmouth
KINGSTON ON   K7L 5A6

Dear Mr. Thomsen:

Thank you for your letter of April 5, 2002 in which you provided a copy of a presentation you were asked to prepare by the Honourable Bob Runciman, Ontario Minister of Economic Development and Trade.

It was thoughtful of you to provide a copy of "Ontario Eat and Live Smart". Your comments with respect to maintaining health have been noted. As I pass the halfway point in the public consultation process, I am overwhelmed by the public response to our call for participation. Canadians have very strong views about how to fix our national health care system and a deep commitment to it. In addition, I have noticed a call for a greater emphasis on wellness and prevention. Your perspective is particularly helpful in my deliberations.

Thank you for your input into the consultation process.

Sincerely,

Roy Romanow
Commissioner

62

Dalton McGuinty, M.P.P. / député
Leader of the Official Opposition
Chef de l'opposition officielle

Room 381
Legislative Building
Queen's Park
Toronto, Ontario
M7A 1A4
(416) 325-7155
(416) 325-9895 fax

Bureau 381
Assemblée Législative
Queen's Park
Toronto (Ontario)
M7A 1A4
(416) 325-7155
(416) 325-9895 téléc.

June 27, 2002

Mr. Volker Thomsen
President and CEO
St. Lawrence College
King and Portsmouth
Kingston, Ontario
K7L 5A6

Dear Mr. Thomsen:

Thank you very much for sending me information on your "Ontario Eat and Live Smart" proposal. It was a pleasure to hear from you. I, too, enjoyed meeting you this past spring.

It is essential that we explore concrete means of taking the pressure off our overburdened health care system. I agree that the benefits of prevention—including educating the public about healthy lifestyle choices—are multifaceted and will save the system countless dollars. I also appreciate your proactive approach to making post-secondary education more affordable and accessible.

I have scanned your proposal and look forward to having an opportunity to review it more thoroughly. I have also forwarded a copy to my Policy and Research staff for further study.

Mr. Thomsen, thank you again for sharing this interesting information with me. I value your views and look forward to an ongoing dialogue with you on these vital issues. Please accept my best wishes for a great summer.

Yours truly,

Dalton McGuinty, MPP
Leader of the Official Opposition
Leader of the Ontario Liberal Party

/mm

www.ontarioliberal.com

Minister of Health Ministre de la Santé

The Honourable/L'honorable A. Anne McLellan

Ottawa, Canada K1A 0K9

JUN 2 5 2002

Mr. Volker Thomsen
President and Chief Executive Officer
St. Lawrence College
King and Portsmouth
Kingston, Ontario K7L 5A6

Dear Mr. Thomsen:

Thank you for your correspondence of April 5, 2002, in which you request a meeting with me to discuss your proposal, *Ontario Eat and Live Smart*.

Unfortunately, prior commitments prevent me from meeting with you at this time. However, I would like to take this opportunity to say that as Minister of Health, I am committed to improving the health and well-being of all Canadians, particularly our children and youth, and I commend you for your interest in promoting healthy lifestyles within Ontario.

I recognize that there are several behaviours such as smoking, obesity, physical inactivity and inadequate nutrition that contribute to increased incidence of many chronic diseases including heart disease, stroke, cancer and diabetes. At the national level, considerable collaborative work has begun around chronic disease prevention, namely in the formation of the Chronic Disease Prevention Alliance of Canada. This group is composed of 12 national professional organizations including the Heart and Stroke Foundation, the Canadian Cancer Society, the Canadian Diabetes Association, the Canadian Council on Tobacco Control, Dieticians of Canada, Coalition on Active Living and Health Canada. Together, these organizations are building on the strengths and expertise that each have individually brought to the table to develop an action plan for a comprehensive, sustainable integrated system of research, surveillance, policies and programs to maintain health and prevent chronic disease. Similar collaborative efforts are beginning in many provinces.

Canada

- 2 -

In Ontario, Health Canada has developed partnerships with provincial and municipal governments, as well as national and provincial non-governmental organizations in an effort to promote active, healthy living. Health Canada has funded initiatives through the Canadian Diabetes Strategy that collaborate with many municipal Heart Health partners in an effort to create comprehensive and effective community planning and programming.

The Ontario Physical and Health Education Association, in collaboration with the Ontario Ministry of Education and Training, has developed a physical activity curriculum for teachers of all elementary grade students that will facilitate quality daily physical education for students. The curriculum provides teachers with the tools and resources that they require to make physical activity enjoyable for the diverse spectrum of students in the education system. The Nutrition Resource Centre housed at the Ontario Public Health Association is also providing nutrition resources for teachers that can be used with students.

There is increasing evidence indicating that the promotion of lifestyle alone is not effective in creating lasting behaviour change. Studies indicate that action on the social determinants of health is a critical factor that also must be addressed. Health Canada is interested in the determinants of health and is working with our many provincial and community partners to address factors such as poverty, social isolation, culture, gender and environment and the impact these factors have on health and well-being.

If you would like to discuss Health Canada initiatives in Ontario that support active, healthy living, please feel free to contact Ms. Freda Burkholder, Adult Health Manager, Population and Public Health Branch, Ontario/Nunavut Region, at the following address:

> 25 St. Clair Avenue East
> 4th Floor
> Toronto, Ontario M4T 1M2
>
> Telephone: (416) 952-1286
> Facsimile: (416)-973-0009

Thank you again for writing.

Yours sincerely,

A. Anne McLellan

What Do We Learn from These Responses?

It is quite clear that all parties are trapped somehow in the present health care system. This is really a "sacred cow" nobody dares to slaughter. We do not want to go away from a public system because of the justifiable fear we would create a divided society of some people who can afford to pay for quality service and others who cannot.

As I am proposing in the report "Canada Eat and Live Smart," we can actually avoid leaving the public system and at the same time create a quality system with first-class service by creating awareness and some conditions that will ensure that people use the system in a responsible and economically feasible way.

Through all the measures proposed, we will be able to save in the neighbourhood of, at least, 1 percent per annum, accumulating, for example, up to 30 percent over thirty years. When we add the planned increase in spending of 20 billion for the same period, it amounts to $30 billion annual savings reached in year ten. *This will result in improved health and a future savings of hundreds of billions of tax dollars!*

The improvement in well-being and health will be even more important than the initial direct savings. In reality, we do not have another choice. We need to go back to a better lifestyle and a better quality of life. The sooner we start on this journey, the better off we will be. We can under no circumstances pay more for health care or let our health deteriorate in a way that we all end up with civilization diseases like cancer, obesity, diabetes, allergies, heart disease, etc. If we don't change our lifestyle and our modern eating habits, it must be feared that the prolonged lifespan that was created as a blessing of civilization through improved hygiene, better medical services and more wealth will soon be drastically reduced again. A large percentage (around 40 percent) of the present generation of young Canadians is in such a bad shape that they will face great challenges to reach the age of forty or fifty!

It is somewhat encouraging to see elements of this kind of thinking in the Liberal provincial and federal platform, but a real commitment to change appears to still be missing.

As pointed out in the report, among other things we need to implement are the following measures:

1. Install a Central Agency for "Innovation and Job Creation" at the Prime Minister's office with liaison at all federal ministers' offices and provincial premiers' offices. Do this together with the opposition, as proposed in the Vision for 2020. The newly installed National Committee on Health could be one important piece in the puzzle.

2. Reform all early-childhood, primary, secondary, college and university curriculum to include a focus on proper food, sports and a healthy lifestyle.

3. Include a minimum of three hours of physical activity daily in all public and private early-childhood programs and include minimum standards of daily and weekly physical activity for schools and other educational institutes.

4. Revise the Food and Drug Act to accommodate the same rules for all food products and drugs. If a modern society like Denmark, for example, can ban trans fatty acids completely, why can we not be equally progressive?

It will take a little more than mediocre steps to implement the necessary changes or conditions; it will take the kind of political leadership we are expecting from the new Prime Minister of Canada!

It will take a vision like "Canada Eat and Live Smart," some courage and a medium- to long-range plan that can lead us beyond a four-year political term!

It will take real leadership!

Chapter Four

Preparing Canadians to Lead Industrial Innovation in All Areas Including Housing, Transportation, Energy and Communication

Without the proposed reform of our health care system there will not be sufficient funding available for a true **"Innovation Agenda."**

When we analyze Canada's last fifteen years, we can clearly see that parallel to the dramatically increased financial demand from the health care system was a proportional downsizing in most other significant areas.

In Ontario, which represents 40 percent of the Canadian population, education and post-secondary education funding was cut to the extent that we are spending 40 percent below the national average per college student and 18 percent below the national average per university student. Universities are a little better off because they were better able to lobby through long-established alumni organizations and because of their much longer establishment in Canadian society. Alabama is the only other jurisdiction in North America where the funding is at a similar low level. This means that 40 percent of the Canadian population has a much lower chance for educational development than the rest of the country has.

Overall, the rest of Canada is doing better than Ontario. Better funding has created better access, better transfer opportunities and a system where every segment is getting better credit. Transfers are regulated in favour of the students' development (for example, in Alberta, BC and Quebec). Although Canadian universities are able to compete internationally in the area of research, as a nation we are not doing very well in development and commercialization.

In the area of apprenticeships and training, all provinces are doing equally poorly. We do not have sufficient numbers of skilled workers. Schools are not properly preparing our students for careers other than those requiring university degrees. The overall quality of apprenticeships is quite high; however, there are not enough employers willing to train apprentices in sufficient numbers to fill the enormous future gap. When the present generation of hundreds of thousands of immigrant tradespeople retire and leave the workforce, there will be a huge vacuum, unless we increase our efforts now.

The Steering Committee on Reforming Apprenticeships in Ontario started its work in the late nineties. Under the scope of this committee, a new innovative Apprenticeship Co-op Diploma is being launched in 2004 that hopefully will bring a renaissance for this area of post-secondary education. The innovative model will be introduced in the chapter "Apprenticeship Training the Traditional Way and Apprenticeship Training Embedded in a Co-op Diploma."

The majority of Canadians do, unfortunately, have a low opinion of apprenticeships. Therefore it is the hope that the new model will be recognized as something worthwhile to get into and that the public will consider this something less of a dead-end street.

It is encouraging that the federal and provincial governments now are putting a stronger emphasis on the skills' agenda. More commitment should bring additional funding and much better results. The joint effort between Industry Canada and HRDC, "The 2003 Summit on Innovation and Learning," was a nice try but did not bring a clear commitment to improve the weak areas of skills, applied research, development and commercialization.

As a participant at both the regional and national summits, I was initially quite enthusiastic about the process and the possible opportunities. But the nearer the national summit got to the end, the more it became clear to me that Industry Minister Allan Rock was not really inclined to go in a new direction. In spite of HRDC Minister Jane Stewart's passionate commitment, it became obvious that there was neither a synchronized vision nor combined leadership.

The enclosed letter of serious concern to Jane Stewart, which was copied to Hon. Allan Rock, Minister of Industry Canada, and the Prime Minister Jean Chrétien, lists most of the shortfalls and worries and has, in spite of the letters of acknowledgement, never been addressed properly.

We must therefore fear that the planned additional spending of $10 billion for Innovation and Learning will mainly flow into the area of university research and not sufficiently into the areas of skills development, applied research, development and commercialization.

Particularly the area of commercialization combined with applied research will in the future need a much stronger focus if Canada wants to be among the leading industrial nations. Canada's ranking among the leading industrial innovators was, until the end of last century, at ninth place in spite of in size being among the seven leading nations. Between then and now, it has dropped to sixteenth place. Three of the four small Scandinavian countries are among the first five, with tiny Finland being number one.

How can we now effectively change our thinking away from the negative or stagnating development and engage all players, including the entire population, to get ready for a turnaround? Even if this sounds like a massive task, the situation is not very different from having a puzzle in front of you, knowing that all pieces are present and you just need to put them together in the right sequence. With thousands of pieces in front of you, the conclusion could be that you can't make it. On the other hand, you can take the initiative to start sorting them, and once you have created the first part of the picture or the "vision," things find their place with ease.

Therefore, preparing Canadians to lead industrial innovation, we must embrace every single piece of the puzzle including our understanding that industrial innovation is only a part of an overall economic, social and cultural development. Once we realize the holistic aspect of success, we will be able to define our vision and move forward, just like the puzzle player who moves forward in a determined way and actually brings the puzzle to conclusion much faster than anticipated.

Innovation Summit documents

COPY

November 26, 2002

The Hon. Jane Stewart, Minister
Human Resources and Development Canada
Room 103-5 Center Block
House of Commons
Ottawa, ON K1A 0A6

Re: Meeting at the National Summit on Innovation and Learning

Dear Ms Stewart: *Jane*

Your passionate delivery of both the Prime Minister's speech and your own presentation for the summit made a deep impression on me. The short meeting with you, together with Mr. Michael Grimaldi (President General Motors Canada), was quite inspiring. I was also very honored and thankful for your public statement about my thinking and focus being correct.

I am always excited and happy when I am meeting with and watching professional leaders or visionaries, particularly those who are passionate and dedicated about what they are doing. It makes a big difference.

The reason for my participation in both the Regional and the National Summit is my great concern that we here in Canada are, to a great extent, unintentionally betting on the wrong horse.

The misleading direction starts within our school system, where we are focusing on preparing every student for university. The same thing is repeated when our expectations of the universities is that they are the birthplace of innovation and development.

There is of course a need for research at universities. There are also some good results coming out of universities, but it is questionable to what extent, because these results tend mostly to be pure research. We need to identify how much focus to put on pure research, how much on applied research and how much on commercialization. All are of significance, and to ignore the importance of the latter two for the sake of the first is to the detriment of society as a whole.

Most innovation and development comes out of small and medium companies. Second on the list are the big corporations, and only the smallest number of new ideas and innovative products actually comes out of universities.

Most research and even most patents end up in an archive, where they are buried, forgotten and with them all the investments and all the effort that went into them.

Therefore I can see a great and exigent need for innovative Leadership that will direct activities in a more pragmatic and applied way.

Office
of the
President
and
Board of
Governors

*A passion
for lifelong learning...*

King & Portsmouth
Kingston, Ontario
K7L 5A6
Tel: (613) 544-5400
Fax: (613) 545-3926

www.sl.on.ca

ISO 9001 Registered

During my conversation at the summit with Michael Grimaldi, I learned that General Motors is spending around 30 Billion $ US on so called research of which a maximum of 20 % is pure research, while the bulk of the funding, around 80 %, is for commercialization and applied research.

At small companies this proportion could easily be even more in favor of applied research and the commercialization.

I participated in the group for **Improving Research, Development and Commercialization. The messages I heard there loud and clearly endorsed what I have stated above.**

The final summary we received at the end of the summit also indicates some of this thinking. However it is not clear enough, and the statement that there is strong support for doubling of R&D investments could easily be misleading, especially if it again relates to putting the main focus on universities.

I am sharing all this with you because it will take all of your leadership, the leadership of the Hon. Allan Rock, and the Government of Canada, to make sure that the tremendous amount of effort that went into this summit will lead to the innovation in learning and products for which we are aiming. In respect to the learning, I want to refer you to my last letter dated October 30, 2002, wherein I explained in detail the challenges and opportunities in respect to basic skills, and the critically needed reform for apprenticeships.

Please feel free to call on me for any possible additional input.

Sincerely yours,

Volker Thomsen
President and CEO

Cc: The Hon. Jean Chretien
The Hon. Allan Rock
The Hon. Peter Milliken
Mr. Joe Jordan
Mr. Peter Adams

COPY

November 26, 2002

Hon. Allan Rock, Minister
Industry Canada
11th Floor, East Tower
C.D. Howe Building
235 Queen Street
Ottawa ON K1A 0H5

Re: National Summit

Dear Mr. Rock:

It was a great pleasure and honour to meet you during the summit and to be introduced to you by the Hon. Jane Stewart after the dinner Monday night.

I was very impressed about the process around both the Regional and the National Summit.

I think that most participants would share my feelings; we did get the impression that
both you and the Hon. Jane Stewart really value our concerns, our feedback and our input.

Because of this, I am sending you and your Deputy Minister Mr. Peter Harder a copy today of my letter to the Hon. Jane Stewart. I hope that it will be helpful for your own final summary of the summit.

Sincerely yours,

Volker Thomsen
President & CEO

Office
of the
President
and
Board of
Governors

*A passion
for lifelong learning...*

King & Portsmouth
Kingston, Ontario
K7L 5A6
Tel: (613) 544-5400
Fax: (613) 545-3926

www.sl.on.ca

ISO 9001 Registered

COPY

St. Lawrence
COLLEGE

October 31, 2002

Hon. Jane Stewart, Minister
Human Resources and Development Canada
Room 103-5 Center Block
House of Commons
Ottawa, ON K1A 0A6

Re: Meeting at the ACCC Conference Oct. 09, 2002 in Ottawa

Dear Ms Stewart:

My colleagues and I were very impressed with the opportunity to exchange some thoughts with you. Your energetic leadership is refreshing and your warmth touches us very much.

I am referring to my answer in respect to apprenticeship training.
After the meeting it became clear to me that it is very important that you get the actual details about reform opportunities of this very important educational and training issue. Without a properly functioning basic skills/ trades training programme, Canada will be in deep trouble. We are already seeing the first signs. Try to get a plumber to come to your home!

You are right that all parties involved need to work together in a constructive way, and I cannot see a reason why the construction unions and colleges cannot work well together. The construction unions are training a good part of the construction-related apprenticeships, which represent approximately 12 % of all programmes, and the colleges are teaching and training the remaining apprenticeships, which represent around 88 % of the whole.

In order for the colleges to get enough interested students to enroll in apprenticeships, these must first be reformed in a way that they are integrated into the college system as part of a seamless system starting in high school and even in some cases ending at the applied degree level.

Because of my background as a tradesperson, and as a long-time entrepreneur in the global food business with production facilities and offices in 20 countries, I have been asked to lead the reform of apprenticeships in Ontario. In this present process St. Lawrence College has developed a career-building system that initially will **integrate all the non-construction apprenticeships in a college diploma** with a co-op partnership with industry and other employers. These improvements will make apprenticeships so much more appealing to parents, students and employers that there will be dramatic increases in enrolment.

There is no doubt that this would eliminate the present shortage of skilled trades people, and the Ministry of Training Colleges and University Training Branch is presently finalizing the details based on a modified version of the original SLC paper.

Office
of the
President
and
Board of
Governors

*Expanding
Opportunities...*

King & Portsmouth
Kingston, Ontario
K7L 5A6
Tel: (613) 544-5400
Fax: (613) 545-3926

www.sl.on.ca

The proposed model also offers University graduates the entrance into a fast track of these trade diploma programs. How can one be a good architect without knowing how to use and apply building materials, for example, properly?

Because of its innovative approach, SLC is one of the fastest-growing colleges in Canada. Based on the KPI (Key Performance Indicators of the Ontario Ministry of Training Colleges and Universities) we are the overall leader in the province (KPI Data attached).

In this connection, I would like to bring your attention to the huge difference in student funding across the country. Ontario college students are presently funded 40 % below the national average (comparison attached). The educational landscape is drifting more and more apart. I support the idea of provincial leadership in education, but I find it unfortunate that there is no true national agenda or leadership on educational standards and direction.

We are leading other innovative initiatives for the future:

> ➤ Eastern Ontario as a centre for renewable energy (Wind, Fuel Cells, Solar, Biomass etc.)

> ➤ St. Lawrence Music & Arts Festival in Eastern Ontario and Northern New York.

We are enclosing some newspaper articles about these highlights for your information.

In January 2002, St. Lawrence College opened its Ottawa Ontario Job Connect storefront operation in partnership with Youth Services Ottawa on 71 Bank Street (a stone's throw away from your present office). As a separate letter, I am sending you, and our Kingston, Brockville, Cornwall and other area MPs, an invitation for our official opening Nov. 27 from 4 to 6 PM. We hope that if you should be available that you would be willing to accept our invitation.

If you need any kind of information and assistance from an independent source please feel free to contact me. Based on my more than 30 years of global entrepreneurship before I joined SLC I still have the ability to maintain a free spirit and an independent opinion.

I am only an hour and a half away from Ottawa, and if needed I would be honoured to be at your service.

Best personal regards,

Volker Thomsen
President and CEO

List of people who have received copies of the letters to the Hon. Jane Stewart and the Hon. Allan Rock:

Mr. Jean Chretien, Prime Minister

Mr. Peter Milliken, M.P. Kingston and the Islands, Speaker of the House of Commons

The Hon. Denis Coderre, Minister of Immigration

Mr. Peter Harder, Deputy Minister, Industry Canada

Mr. Paul Martin, MP

Mr. Joe Jordan, M.P.

Mr. Peter Adams, M.P. (who forwarded the letter to the Hon. John Manley, Minister, Finance).

Mr. Jeff Garrah, Chief of Staff for Mr. Peter Milliken

Mr. Mac Harb, M.P.

Mr. Bryon Wilfert, M.P. Oak Ridges

Mr. Michael Grimaldi, President, General Motors of Canada

Minister
of Human Resources
Development

Ministre
du Développement
des ressources humaines

Ottawa, Canada K1A 0J9

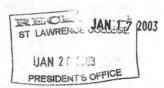

RECD JAN 17 2003
ST LAWRENCE COLLEGE

UAN 2 0 2003
PRESIDENT'S OFFICE

Mr. Volker Thomsen
President and Chief Executive Officer
St. Lawrence College
King and Portsmouth
Kingston, Ontario
K7L 5A6

Dear Mr. Thomsen:

Thank you for your letter of November 26, 2002, in which you shared your concerns in regards to Canada's education and research system, as well as the enclosed pamphlet entitled *Study in Canada: Where learning is fun* ...

It was a pleasure to meet you in the context of the National Summit on Innovation and Learning, held in Toronto on November 18 and 19, 2002. I always appreciate discussing issues of mutual interest with you and being informed of your point of view. I was delighted by the Summit's resounding success which is due, undoubtedly, to the active participation of so many dedicated people, like you, ready to contribute to make Canada a more innovative and inclusive country.

With respect to the important role played by small and medium enterprises (SMEs) in innovation, you will be interested to know that Human Resources Development Canada and Industry Canada, in collaboration with the Canadian Manufacturers and Exporters and the Association of Community Colleges of Canada, are bringing together representatives of SMEs, community colleges, key sector councils and other relevant agencies to explore ways to support SMEs through better access to expertise at community colleges and institutes of technology.

In reference to your letter of last October concerning learning issues, you will recall that I announced at the National Summit that the Government of Canada is investing $12 million in a partnership with the Canadian Apprenticeship Forum and Skills Canada to launch a marketing campaign on apprenticeship. We believe it is important to send a strong message to Canadian parents, young people and employers on the importance of skilled trades and the opportunities they offer for good and rewarding careers. This is in addition to the support we already provide, through various means, to apprenticeship.

...../2

- 2 -

As research and development issues fall directly under Industry Canada's purview, my colleague, the Honourable Allan Rock, Minister of Industry, could provide you v further information on this subject. I note that Minister Rock has been copied on your letter a am sure he will be pleased to reply to your concerns.

Again, thank you for taking the time to write.

Sincerely,

Jane Stewart, P.C., M.P.

c.c. The Honourable Allan Rock, P.C., M.P.
      The Honourable Peter Milliken, P.C., M.P.
      Mr. Peter Adams, M.P.
      Mr. Joe Jordan, M.P.

Minister
of Human Resources
Development

Ministre
du Développement
des ressources humaines

Ottawa, Canada K1A 0J9

JAN 1 7 2003

Mr. Volker Thomsen
President and Chief Executive Officer
St. Lawrence College
King & Portsmouth
Kingston, Ontario
K7L 5A6

Dear Mr. Thomsen:

Thank you for your letter of October 31, 2002, concerning apprenticeship training. While respecting provincial and territorial authority over apprenticeship training programs, Human Resources Development Canada (HRDC) recognizes that every effort must be made to increase apprenticeship training enrollment and completion rates in order to address skills shortages across Canada. An adequate supply of skilled trades workers is the key to keeping Canada economically strong and socially sound.

In February, HRDC reaffirmed its commitment to the skilled trades when the document *Knowledge Matters: Skills and Learning for Canadians* set the milestone of doubling the number of apprentices completing a certification program to 37,000 in 10 years. HRDC will work toward this milestone with its partners in the apprenticeship community through the Canadian Apprenticeship Forum (CAF), a multi-partite organization that brings together national business and labour groups, the Inter-Provincial Alliance of Apprenticeship Board Chairs, educators and the Canadian Council of Directors of Apprenticeship.

Recently, HRDC has taken two steps toward achieving this milestone. On June 2, 2002, I announced that the department would assist in the creation of an apprenticeship Inventory and Information System. In November 2002, I also announced HRDC funding in the amount of $12 million for CAF and Skills Canada to jointly undertake a campaign to promote skilled trades as a solid career choice for young Canadians. Together, these two projects will increase awareness of apprenticeship training systems across Canada and contribute to higher levels of recruitment and retention. These projects are examples of a coordinated approach to increasing Canada's supply of skilled trades workers. Should you wish to obtain further information on these projects, I encourage you to contact Mr. Keith Lancastle, CAF Executive Director, at (613) 235-4004 extension 203.

...2

Canada

Given our department's commitment to Canada's apprenticeship system, I was pleased to hear that St. Lawrence College is also developing innovative solutions to increase the supply of skilled trades workers by proposing modifications to the college system to the Ontario Ministry of Training, Colleges and Universities. Through generating new ideas and sustaining strong partnerships, the apprenticeship community will find success in ensuring an ample supply of skilled workers for the future.

Thank you again for sharing your views and for your continued participation and interest in apprenticeship.

Sincerely,

Jane Stewart, P.C., M.P.

What Are We Learning from the Responses? Did the Summit Bring Innovation and Learning to the Forefront?

Since the summit, the leadership in government has changed but the speed of implementation seems to be unchanged. Several years of planning and the regional and national summit expenses in the millions cannot have been wasted completely. Hopefully we will soon see an agenda and action plan that will identify the many opportunities we have and move forward in a fashion that will guide us "Enroute to Prosperity."

What is the Reason for Scandinavia's Stunning Success?

Having known and participated in the both Scandinavian and Canadian development as an entrepreneur since 1962, I am actually not at all surprised. During these past forty years, these countries evolved from being mainly agricultural societies to

81

leaders in innovation and success. This did not happen by coincidence. The Scandinavian countries tried early on to create a competitive counterbalance to the very aggressive and modern industrial societies like Germany, Holland, Belgian and France in the south, more traditional industrial societies in the UK and Ireland in the southwest and emerging industrial societies in Russia, Lithuania, Estonia, Lithia, Poland, Chechen, Slovakia and Hungary in the southeast.

The Scandinavian countries detected early on that they had to be more innovative in every respect to compete and make up for their distance from the main markets. You can only be better and succeed in a location like Scandinavia or Canada if you have access to good raw materials. But this is not enough; you must also have skilled people who develop and produce innovative, well-styled, quality products that are able to compete in the major central markets.

Scandinavian Education and Training

All Scandinavian countries have an integrated middle- and high-school system. Students who are not inclined to go in an academic direction are early on encouraged and supported in their journey to an equally successful non-academic career. The system is built so that anybody at a later date can continue to build on the various segments of their education and training, similar to the Danish toy "Lego" that is a never-ending play experience with one segment supporting the next. We could call this the "Lego" system of education.

In addition to primary and secondary middle- and high-school education, there are very strong vocational/skills training schools (*teknisk hoejskole*), trade and commerce colleges (*handelshoejskole*) and continuing education colleges/vocational schools (*hoejskole*). The university system, with centres of excellence, is also integrated in the overall well-functioning system. The traditional apprenticeship still plays a much more significant role than in Canada. In Northern Europe, apprenticeships are just as respected as the other parts of the overall integrated system.

This very diversified system creates the right mix of well-educated, trained and skilled people for all the needs of a modern industrial society.

The Role of the "Technology Centre"

Many, primarily smaller, Scandinavian communities in the sixties and even earlier started to create so-called "Technology Centres." These were in reality slightly more sophisticated small industrial or business parks that would help and encourage emerging technical companies to move in together and benefit from some joint services and installations. This created an industrial climate outside the bigger industrial areas, which resulted in a tremendous boost for thousands of small innovative companies in smaller communities.

I want to mention some gigantic success stories of companies that evolved out of this climate:

Denmark

"Lego" in Billund: Although this company was founded before technology centres evolved, it is a typical example. A small carpenter shop in a small rural community after World War II developed into the largest and most successful toy company of all times. The village of Billund in Jytland is still Lego's centre and the seat of its head office from where a multi-billion dollar, very innovative global toy business is operated. Although Billund has a population of only a few thousand people, it has an international airport where jumbo jets are landing daily and bringing thousands of visitors to the world famous "Legoland."

Ecco Shoes: One of the largest global shoe manufacturers, with factories all over the world.

Novo Pharm: The world's biggest provider of insulin and the maker of many renown pharmaceuticals.

Danish Butter Cookies: Together from twenty different rural communities, control some of the most successful international cookie brands produced today.

Vestas/NEG MICON and Nordex: The world's largest producers of wind turbines. Tens of thousands of people in Denmark are employed in wind and other renewable energies. More than 20 percent of the home market electricity needs are supplied by renewable energy. There is a great awareness in the entire population about the importance of conserving energy and living in tune with the environment.

Denmark has so many of these kinds of companies that I could continue for many pages with thousands of small- and medium-sized companies that are leaders in furniture, silverware, textiles, high tech, sailboats, wind turbines, solar panels, communications, entertainment, etc.

Sweden

Sweden is the only small country in the world that produces two global automotive brands, **Volvo and Saab.** With eight million inhabitants it has a relatively insignificant home market but is one of the world leaders in global brands and companies. **Volvo, SAAB, Ericsson, Electrolux, ABB, Astra Zeneca, Pharmacia, Atlas Copco, SKF, Ikea, and Tetra Pak** are some examples.

Sweden's success was like Canada's success, originally based on Sweden's rich resources, including a significant amount of hydro power, paper and steel. Today's great success stories, however, are mainly based on human resources and innovation. Beside IT and telecom, biomedicine is also looked on as one of the most important industries of the future.

Alfred Nobel (1833-1896), as an inventor, chemist and industrial prize donor, helped to create the Swedish image. Even today the Nobel Prize stands for change, creation and innovation.

Finland

Although Finland until the early 1990s was limping behind other Scandinavian countries in overall development, it did not take long to change this. The biggest breakthrough followed in that decade and led to Finland becoming the Industrial Output and Innovation world leader in 2003.

There are similar stunning examples of the turnaround in the other Scandinavian countries. I want to mention a few of the most remarkable examples:

Nokia: Today Nokia is one of the best known global companies. Nokia evolved out of a conglomerate of struggling paper industries and transformed into a high-tech group in telecommunications and mobile phones. They control almost 50 percent of the mobile phone world market and, in spite of fierce global competition, their market share is still growing.

Valmet: Originally a state-owned company, Valmet was privatized in 1996 and is today considered a world leader in paper machines.

Kvaerner-Masa- Yards: This shipbuilder has survived and succeeded in a top salary market like Finland and is leading particularly in specialty shipbuilding in the world.

Today, Finland has smart homes, smart energy, smart communication and smart transportation. We can conclude that this is a land of smart people who also eat and live smart! Finland is a tremendous success for a country of only 5 million people.

Norway

Like Canada, Norway is a very beautiful country. Many areas resemble British Columbia; other areas remind you of Newfoundland; and yet you will find spots like PEI, Quebec and Ontario. Norway stretches more than 2000 km from Northern

Jytland (Denmark) all the way to Spitzbergen, one the most northerly areas of Europe.

Norway has only been a sovereign state for a little more than ninety-five years. For many years it was ruled from Denmark and later in partnership with Sweden. This helps to explain why Norway has taken a different route than other Scandinavian countries.

There is no doubt that Norwegians are just as talented and entrepreneurial as the rest of Scandinavia. But it has chosen to take another avenue, neither participating in the European Union nor in the EURO currency. On one hand this has resulted in a great independence but on the other hand it has also created some isolation from certain developments. Economically, Norway is strong. It has large reserves of oil and gas. Traditionally it also has a strong shipping industry, fishing and agriculture.

The 4.5 million Norwegians enjoy a very high standard of living and, even if they do not enjoy the same amount of publicity and marketing successes as their neighbors, they are a culturally integrated part of the Scandinavian success story.

Altogether greater Scandinavia, including Finland, Denmark, Sweden, Norway, Iceland (another very successful small country of 260,000 people), Greenland and the Faeroes, has an entire population of less than 24 million people, or approximately 80 percent of the Canadian population.

Scandinavia as a group of countries or people has created more world-class products and successes of every kind than most other much larger nations. Therefore, and also because of the many similarities in population background, geography, and to some extent history, **Scandinavia is a great inspiration for Canada.**

These many Scandinavian examples have one thing in common. Top design, top quality and functionality are combined with innovative visionary ideas. These achievements, together with living in tune with nature and embracing every possible form of renewable energy, have created a climate of prosperity and success!

How Can Canada Catch Up with Leading Innovators like Scandinavia and What Are the Areas of Priority?

Reading the Scandinavian success stories, we may tend to be skeptical and doubt our own ability to create something similarly extraordinary. Having lived in Scandinavia, Germany, Canada, China and many other areas, I do not for one moment doubt that we in Canada have equal or even better opportunities. There is hardly any raw product that is not available in abundance and at a good price; space is plentiful and very reasonable. There is access to resources of all kinds, including a good pool of talented people; first-class schools, colleges and universities; good government services; a good infrastructure; a healthy banking and investment community; and access to substantial venture capital.

Because of limited corruption in Canada and a fair playing field, there are good chances to develop and prosper in spite of some dominance by big players.

What Main Hurdles Are Preventing Us from Being Innovative World Market Leaders?

I can detect one main hurdle: a big mental block. We Canadians have a reluctance to adopt change quickly and a strong reliance on the big market south of the border. The proximity to the U.S. market, the dependence on this market and the willingness to accept this situation, letting big brother determine our direction and fate, hold back Canadian innovation.

We should fully endorse a good partnership with our neighbours in the U.S.A., but we must develop many additional markets and partnerships! In recent years, more and more Canadians have felt the need to create a much more distinctly Canadian way of doing business and of living our lives. We want a distinctly Canadian foreign policy.

83 percent of all Canadian exports go to the U.S.A. and only 17 percent to the rest of the world. If we could turn these figures around we would be talking about a much healthier balance. If we

look at other jurisdictions we can clearly see a difference. The biggest trading partners and direct neighbours in Europe, France and Germany, do less than 10 percent of their trade with each other.

Canada is in a situation similar to Scandinavia. Therefore, if we analyze what did they do right and what mistakes are to be avoided, we will find a route to the kind of prosperity and success we are dreaming about.

Just as Scandinavian countries became independent of their dominating, neighbouring markets and began to understand that diversification in markets and products can be just as important as the ownership of vast resources, including well qualified people, we as Canadians must also learn that we only will be able to remain independent as a nation if we create a similar strategy. This doesn't preclude us from living in respectful harmony with our neighbours. The opposite is actually the case. The more self-realization and direction we develop, the more likely will we be to maintain our neighbour's respect and support.

Chapter Five

Canada Is Far Behind in Developing Green and/or Renewable Energy

We can turn this around by introducing federal/provincial policy and atandards on new kinds of energy.

It is very interesting to discover that the leading nations in innovation and productivity are all embracing clean technologies in the generation of power, transportation and waste management. As Canadians, we have for many years enjoyed "unlimited" resources and vast space, clean water and clean air.

This picture is changing rapidly. In our highly populated areas, pollution levels and the scarcity of clean water and clean air are easily at the same level as those in other industrial nations. It always stuns me that living on one of the Thousand Islands in the St. Lawrence, relatively far away from heavily industrialized areas, we experience more than thirty days of smog per year.

Even if part of the pollution is imported, most of it is homemade. The disaster around the drinking water in Walkerton shows us that intensive animal farming quickly changes the quality of the drinking water in a way that is a direct threat to our health. The same goes for air quality. Because of the huge air space, this results in minor effects today, but a large part of our population suffers from respiratory illnesses or allergies of one kind or the other.

Nothing is gained by blaming one or more segments of our society. Assigning blame to the farming industry for polluting the water or to the generating stations for polluting the air will not get us out of the hole. We need to address all issues in a responsible way, including all players and all parts of our society. Responsible standards that cover all areas of activity will be the only way to ensure that we leave an environment for our children that will enable life to continue. Many countries, such as Germany, the UK and Scandinavia, have legislation in place that addresses all the important issues. There is no need for us to reinvent those aspects of necessary legislation; we can learn from countries that have already gone through the learning stages. Using their experience and adding our findings, we could improve and tailor the legislation to our needs.

The challenge in Canada will be to synchronize federal needs and standards with provincial interests. The challenges are opportunities we need to buy into. Considering the magnitude and the significance of it, this goal is another opportunity to show leadership and vision.

The following paper, which I presented at a national conference on solar/renewable energy at Queen's University in August 2003, will give you a fairly detailed overview of what we need to do in Canada to become a serious and respected player in green/renewable energy.

Canada is in a unique position. More than 50 percent of our energy needs are already met through hydro generation, which is ideal to combine with renewables, like sun and wind, that are not available twenty-four hours a day. Capitalizing on these energies will help us to catch up and will catapult us to the top in no time. When I wrote the title of the paper, I was first inclined to write "With True Leadership and Ownership Alternative Energies Will in an Innovative Way Enable Canada to Lead the World to a Spiritual and Industrial Renewal." But considering our Canadian reality, I will for the time being leave the title the way it is.

PRESENTED: SESCI 2003 CONFERENCE QUEEN'S
UNIVERSITY, KINGSTON, ONTARIO, CANADA. AUGUST
18–20, 2003.

WITHOUT TRUE LEADERSHIP AND OWNERSHIP ALTERNATIVE
ENERGIES WILL NOT SUCCEED: THE NEED FOR POLICY CRE-
ATION AND RENEWAL AT THE FEDERAL, PROVINCIAL AND
MUNICIPAL LEVELS.

Abstract

It is clear that Ontario, indeed, Canada as a whole, has the ability
to evolve as a world centre of excellence in alternative energies.
All alternative energies should continue to be considered, discussed and developed, including wind generation, fuel cells, solar
power, bio mass and alternative fuels, to name but a few. In this
way, all fields of alternative energy generation will benefit by
gaining momentum from areas of successful development. It is
this holistic view of alternative energies that will provide the
most significant benefit to our environment, our businesses and
industries, and, perhaps most importantly, our homes.

There is rapid growth in renewable energy worldwide. More
wind power generation systems have been built worldwide in
each of the past six years than any other form of power; however,
due to its historic reliance on nuclear, fossil and large hydro
energy production systems, Ontario has not benefited from this
trend. Ontario is now experiencing a shortfall in electrical production as a result of the fact that no fossil or hydro plants have
been built in more than ten years. This problem can be alleviated
with new, renewable power generation. The Kyoto Accord and
public opinion will quickly result in these projects becoming
mandatory for Canada. What is now needed is a set of holistic
policies at all levels of government: federal, provincial, and
municipal. These policies should cover all the forms of alternative energies that can be utilized. Strong and effective leadership
is paramount in order to achieve these policy goals, if the drive

toward recognition and utilization of alternative energies is to succeed. The impact on types of systems and energies that can be utilized will be discussed, as will the need for public education in order to achieve our goals.

Introduction

The Kingston area, to give just one example, has an enormous potential to generate clean, renewable power from wind and small hydro projects and thus could see local investments of $300-500 million within less than five years. Local manufacturing, development, construction and service jobs would be created within the Eastern Ontario region. It is estimated that about 35 percent of the investment in renewable energy would be made in area businesses. Federal and provincial incentives have been announced that make this initiative possible if carried out now. Simple and cost effective additions to these programs would guarantee that the rush to renewable energy systems, seen in Europe, U.S.A., Japan and elsewhere, would also begin in Kingston. However, due to slow implementation and/or poorly thought-out processes, this investment is not happening. Eastern Ontario area politicians are in a position to demand that these programs be implemented so the area can benefit from the resulting private investment. This is a template that could be followed in other areas of the province and the country.

The Challenges

To use this area as our continuing example, Eastern Ontario is served primarily by electricity generated from the fossil-fired Lennox Generating Station, in addition to nuclear power from the Darlington plant near Toronto. Small hydro plants on the Rideau system also provide limited local generation. Minimal local employment is provided, and there are no incentives to capitalize on the burgeoning demand for new power generation. An internationally acclaimed hydro manufacturer is located in Eastern Ontario, although local sales from this firm are non-existent. Kingston has the industry and skills to manufacture energy generation products, particularly for hydro and wind power. Kingston is also a centre of excellence and possesses strong research and technical skills to link to the growth of renewable energy. These skills must be developed at home before they can be exported to the quickly growing market of the north eastern US.

Provincial policy has long favoured the expansion of nuclear power, to the detriment of all other sources. This policy focus has resulted in billions of dollars being invested in the GTA and western Ontario. However, these investments are paid for by provincial taxes and provincially supported debt that is then spread throughout the province. There is no potential, under the current regime for Eastern Ontario, to do more than pay heavily to subsidize expansion elsewhere.

To look at this matter in a more global context, we need to consider the sway that the world's developed countries hold over energy politics. As energy industries restructure to cope with both more competition from utilities deregulation and increased environmental regulation, cost-competitive renewable energy sources become more interesting to investors. Widely distributed renewable energy technologies foreground the importance of large sunny and/or windy land areas relative to more geographically concentrated underground hydrocarbon resources. Increasingly, local alternative energies will be able to produce sustainable energies at a lower cost than fossil fuel transported from remote domestic sources, or abroad.

Energy politics are an important aspect of world politics. In world politics, the U.S. is now the only fourfold military-economic-political-technological superpower. Europe is a threefold economic-political-technological superpower. Japan is a twofold economic-technological superpower. Russia remains a military-technological superpower, and China is a political superpower on the way to becoming an economic one. The significance of these

facts of current world politics is that the U.S. and Europe domi-
nate but no longer unilaterally control world energy politics,
which determines world energy trade, investment, and technological progress through trade investments. Almost all the leading
energy companies are still American or European. They have a
vested interest in protecting energy, meaning that they must protect access to the countries that are rich in foreign oil.

As Charles Abt[1] suggests, the options open to the U.S., Europe,
China and Japan to reduce energy import dependence include
resorting to more domestic coal at a heavy environmental cost
(except in Japan); resorting to an unpopular (in the U.S. and
Germany) build-up of nuclear power (which France has accomplished); and investing in indigenous renewable resources such as
solar and wind and bio waste and the technologies to make them
cost-competitive with domestic coal. All four great powers are
pursuing these options that, if pursued effectively, reduce dependence on energy imports, limit the ability of foreign oil and gas
producers to raise prices arbitrarily, provide examples for poor
countries even more energy-import dependent (such as the
Philippines), and improve relations with industrial allies and
energy-importing developing countries. Why should Canada not
pursue the ability to be a leader among nations with increasing
reliance on alternative energies, blessed as we are with the rich
resources to do so? Considering our close ties with Europe,
which has already taken a lead in environmentally sustainable
energy development, why should we not be in the vanguard of
this much needed change in policy focus?

The Opportunities

To return to our local example, Eastern Ontario possesses considerable electricity generation potential. There is well-estab-
lished small hydro generation potential, as well as considerable
wind generation potential along the shores of Lake Ontario and
the St. Lawrence River. Both hydro and wind potentials are
focused in the area of Kingston and the Islands. Tapping into this

resource would bring a considerable number of jobs to the area, encourage local manufacturing and service, and attract tourism, and research and development dollars. In short, Eastern Ontario could become self-sufficient in power, attract investment and increase the quality and reliability of the local power supply.

The provincial government has stated that it wishes to see additional energy generation built in the province. It has also indicated strong support for renewable sources. However, the reality is that power shortfalls are encouraging U.S. coal-fired producers to export large volumes of energy to this province, at high prices. The limited tie-line capacity out of the province, plus ongoing problems with the nuclear program, means that future local power shortages are likely.

The rest of the world, particularly Europe, has already caught on to the necessities of lessening its reliance on fossil fuels, and developing sustainable alternative energies. Wind and solar power play an ever increasing role in Denmark, the Netherlands, Britain, Germany, Norway, Sweden, the Iberian peninsula, and the Adriatic; and solar energy is becoming fully exploited in Spain, France, Italy and Greece. Even the largely underutilized hydroelectric potential of the Balkans is being developed.

Europe is a model for the rest of the world, and Canada can emulate it in North America. Europe has shown that it can substitute non-greenhouse gases-emitting renewable energy for coal and oil, first with hydroelectric power in Switzerland and Norway, then with biomass power in France, in the last decade with wind turbines in Denmark, with energy-independent solar-powered buildings in the Netherlands, Germany and England, and with energy-conserving and non-polluting electric vehicles in France, Italy and Germany. However, all of these things are only possible with political support and political will, and those two things will not happen without strong leadership first from outside our three levels of government, and then later, hopefully, from within.

Policy Concerns

Provincial policy has left the Ontario market bereft of the Power Purchase Agreements ("PPA": a sales contract for electricity) needed to encourage new energy generation. Although it leads the way towards a deregulated electricity market, provincial policy seems short on real incentives to encourage new energy development in the Province of Ontario. Various tax measures have been provided, although the renewable energy industry is quick to point out that these are not enough to bring on new generation.

Federal policy to purchase green power in Ontario, via a PPA, was announced about two years ago but has since been delayed seven times. It appears likely that this program, which has encouraged wind power in some other provinces, will not benefit Ontario in the near future.

However, without a power purchase agreement, no developer can obtain the needed debt financing nor risk venture capital. This hurdle effectively prevents the projects from proceeding. We feel that the help of local politicians is necessary to resolve the issue of power sales. Support could take the form of:

- Encouraging the federal government to make good on its promise to buy green power in Ontario, and/or

- Encouraging the provincial government to follow the recommendations of the Select Committee on Alternative Fuel Sources

Companies like Canadian Renewable Energy Corporation (CREC) Vision Quest, Alberta, Vector in Ottawa and Gaia Power, Kingston, would like to maintain a focus on the finance, construction and operation of renewable projects in the greater Kingston area. These companies are continuing to spend money acquiring land options, studying renewable resources and maintaining an office in the area. However, their experience shows that without local changes at a political level their projects will not proceed. Support from the political arena is now critical if we wish to see renewable energy projects built.

The world picture is also complex. U.S. President George W. Bush has proclaimed that the U.S. government will not ratify or comply with the 1997 Kyoto Protocol on greenhouse gas emissions, global warming and climate change. In May his administration revealed a new energy policy, which included building 1,300 new electric power plants over 20 years, a $2 billion subsidy for the coal industry, reviving a dead nuclear power industry with new subsidies, rolling back clean-air regulations, and drilling for oil and gas in fragile, previously off-limit areas. Conservation and alternative energies received only a footnote.

To quote an editorial from Canadian Dimension2: "There is a mountain of evidence demonstrating that an alternative energy policy is available. North Americans have barely touched energy conservation and efficiency. Public transit, railroads and greater fuel efficiency for vehicles are policies that are being adopted elsewhere. Solar energy has a great potential the technology is improving every day, and it is cheap when all costs are considered. Even in the United Kingdom, photovoltaic roofs are being installed on houses. The American Wind Energy Association claims that the wind power potential in North Dakota, Kansas and Texas would be enough to provide all U.S. national electricity needs and could be developed much quicker than power plants. The U.S. Bonneville Power Administration put out a request for bids for 1,000 megawatts of wind-generating capacity and received enough bids to build 2,600 megawatts. Wind energy now costs between $0.04 and $0.06 per kilowatt-hour, which makes it competitive with coal, and well below the U.S. average cost of $0.085. There is no energy crisis. There is an emissions crisis. And there is a political crisis."

Clearly, under circumstances such as those described above, entry into the market for *any* alternative energy is discouraged. This is the situation we must work to change.

At present the political debate has mainly dealt with *how much* we tax, not *what* we tax. This is unfortunate, for what we tax is important. In most countries the governmental budget relies largely on personal income taxes (salaries and wages) and corporate income taxes that are also taxes on investment and capital gains. In Canada, these taxes exist alongside the GST, provincial taxes and property taxes.

Our present taxes fall mostly on just those activities that make the economy productive: work, savings and investment. Naturally, such taxes discourage people from undertaking these vital activities. A better system would place more of the tax burden on activities that make the economy unproductive and that should be discouraged like resource waste and pollution.

Environmental taxes (charges) are one of several incentive-based instruments of environmental policy. Such taxes and charges are mechanisms for dealing with the systematic failures in market incentives that arise when individual actors do not pay full costs (external costs) of their activities.

Shifting the tax burden away from economic "goods" toward environmental "bads" seems to be inevitable in effective and environmentally friendly policy. Economic productivity and environmental protection are not incompatible and the economy would, as a whole, benefit from this shift.

Leadership: The Time Is Now

Where groups of interested parties come together to press their point is the locus of change for political power and policy-making. To give a small example, at least in the global context, our local group, SWITCH, is a wonderful example of a number of parties, with diverse and sometimes competing interests, coming together to form a powerful lobbying force. I would just caution that the ideal for such groups is that they be able to set aside any individual agendas in recognition of the greater good that the group as a whole may derive from the power of numbers.

Local political involvement is required in order to:

• Obtain public funding to upgrade facilities so as to facilitate alternative energy development. For example, this could include initiatives such as the one to upgrade the interconnection from Wolfe Island to Kingston. This may involve the creation of a public-private transmission company to service Wolfe Island generation.

• Implement a pilot renewable procurement program to assist in resolving the issues the federal government is having in implementing green power purchases in Ontario.

• Create a commitment from the federal government to purchase power from local renewable sources for use in its local area facilities, whatever they may be. Large-scale institutional purchases of green power would help to translate into sales to other commercial interests.

Yet another brief example of how private concerns can help to develop alternate energy resources, with benefits accruing to the local economy, is CREC's completion of a 3 MW small hydro project in Englehart, Ontario, where it spent half of the $6 million capital cost of the project on services from within the Englehart community.

Direct Applications of Alternative Energies

In countries where alternative energies are on the move, all tend to complement one another. It is this holistic view that can help lobbying efforts to change policies. But, to start in a small way, we can all look at ways of using alternative energies, even in our homes. From there we can evolve to larger commercial and industrial uses. Direct applications give us the opportunity to increase conventional awareness of these technologies and their uses. That being said, we will need also to consider changing our view on such matters as how we design and build our houses. Much of our savings, both economically and environmentally, will come from the benefits realized by increasing energy efficiency in our homes and workplaces, in addition to organizing ourselves for waste management and recycling in a completely different way; for example, appropriate sorting of waste materials for use in biomass technologies. There are opportunities to improve how we do things at all levels.

Solar

Solar energy applications are readily available in many parts of the world, given that the technology has advanced to the point that plain good daylight is sufficient for most needs, such as hot water, direct heating, and electricity. Once again, design can play an integral part in how we use the sun's energy in our homes; for example, if we build our homes in such a way that, even without solar arrays, we use the energy that enters our windows efficiently, we can contribute to direct heating. Cynics will point out that this may be detrimental to cooling, say, on a hot summer day. But here again, design and efficiency can help. Designing a home layout so that the use of the sun is directional, and complemented by insulated aluminum blinds to negate unwanted heat, is but one way of handling one specific and oft-cited drawback.

To give a larger and more specific example, we have only to look at the new developments in the buildings here at Queen's. The Integrated Learning Centre's photovoltaic arrays have a second function: they act as sunshades for the building's windows.[2] Once again, we have an example of functional design coupled with power generation capabilities, all in the service of familiarizing future generations of engineers with the concept of renewable and alternative energies.

Another specific direct application that is becoming of interest, particularly in developing countries, is the solar cooker. Some of these are even capable of storing their excess energy in batteries for 2-3 days, thus providing an effective source of food preparation even on less than ideal days.

Wind

In an area like Kingston, it's hard to deny the attractiveness of wind generation as an alternative energy. Blessed as we are with an abundance of wind and more than adequate wind speed, it seems difficult to imagine why we have to fight to develop this potential.

Globally, the present wind technologies are at, or nearing, their peak. Anything beyond a 5 megawatt turbine seems unlikely. The focus now should be on advancing wind as a viable alternative energy and on identifying the most practical sizes and installations of the technology in order to benefit remote areas. For example, Vergnet Canada, the Canadian arm of the French turbine manufacturer, has some interesting models that are simple to install and maintain and do not require large-scale foundations and installation costs. These would be particularly attractive for installations in Canada's far North.

The attractiveness of these technologies also appeals to the individual consumer. There are those who have erected small generators for themselves to supply a specific on-site need; it seems to me that many people are revisiting the benefits of not having to rely completely on the regular grid, particularly after our spectacular ice storm a few years ago. I have even fielded calls from a group hoping to build a small community that would use wind as its primary energy source for individual homes in the Quinte region.

Certainly, it will be grassroots interests such as these that will continue to drive the movement toward sustainable energies.

Biomass

It will also be necessary, I believe, to consider the hybridization of alternative energy systems. Certain technologies lend themselves well to being combined with others, and biomass energy production is certainly one of these.

While biomass includes wood, crop residues, municipal waste, sewage and other organic materials that can be converted for power production and transportation fuels, including ethanol and iodized, it seems likely, looking at the global research that is now occurring, to focus on bio-gasification as a good candidate for our homes and offices.

The conversion of waste materials to useable energy has, at times, been a controversial subject, but with advances in technology it is clearly now a viable alternative energy. The key to being able to use our waste effectively, however, whether on large scales or smaller scales, is proper sorting. Using up our own household waste, including organic garden materials as well as our other "garbage," is a scalable concept that grows to encompass commercial applications to industries and others.

We should not forget that we can also reclaim some of the by-products of such energy production by reclaiming the water that is produced, another significant environmental saving.

I am tempted to state that Walkerton's disaster would not have happened if the vast quantities of animal manure in Southern Ontario had been used in a meaningful way to produce energy instead of polluting the ground water. Communities in Western Denmark along the Atlantic Coast have for many years combined energy production from wind and biomass, and in this way have become self-sufficient.

Some time in the future I can visualize small bioreactors in every household or in groups of households converting organic waste, sewage, garden waste, etc. into gas for cooking, heating and electricity.

Fuel Cells

Not too long ago, during the National Summit for Innovation and Learning in Toronto, I met one of the leading Canadian car manufacturing executives, and we discussed the fantastic opportunities fuel cells offer for cars, for households, etc. When I learned that his perception of the prime source of energy to fuel the cells was based on atomic energy, I realized that we still have to create awareness around the many alternative opportunities.

It is my plan personally to install a fuel cell central heating and electricity generating unit as soon as a household unit can be bought for below $10,000 Canadian. Based on Kingston Fuel Cell Technology Inc., this will happen within the next 3 to 5 years. Exciting prospects!

Conclusions

The success of the future alternative energy policies, not just in Canada but also globally, lies in partnership, experience sharing and multilateral learning, particularly where interested parties can work together to effect policy and political change. Only with this type of holistic approach to leadership will alternative energies succeed.

The International Energy Agency[3] notes that the prices for renewable energies have fallen over the past five years to a point where "most are now cost competitive with fossil technologies when all values are considered." The entrance of these technologies into the mainstream should be a cause for rejoicing; instead we find ourselves fighting to give them the recognition they deserve. This is largely because although the market is robust, it is growing from a fairly small base and requires continuing education efforts on all of our parts.

The agency goes on to say that "a long-term commitment and strategy are needed to ensure renewables are not sidelined, bypassing their full potential...a policy framework must be created that will provide a more level playing field because rules, laws and systems have built up over the last century, based primarily on fossil-fuel based systems."[4]

For alternatives to survive, indeed, flourish, our governments must rectify past imbalances of those old approaches. Our new policies must lead the dynamic changes underway within the energy sector, but at the same time they must also reflect our priorities socially, economically and environmentally. We need to start by requiring, as does the European Union, that a specific percentage of generation must come from renewables. Even with the backward steps that national policy has taken in the U.S., many states are including such policies in their own portfolio standards.

Let us move forward together into the future by ensuring that we succeed in obtaining the policies and policy changes that we know are crucial. Let us put aside our differences, at least in this one arena, and subjugate our various agendas to the greater good of our lives and our planet, and make alternative energy production a vibrant part of the energy sector.

If we understand Kyoto as a symbol for change, Canada will benefit greatly from betting on renewably energy and overall holistic thinking! Together with a re-establishment of a true "agriculture" and a move away from massive farm industries that destroy our environment, we can create a new direction in industry, mining, forestry and farming which will create millions of sustainable jobs and show the leadership for which the rest of the world is looking.

[1] Charles C. Abt, "The Future of Energy, for the Perspective of the Social Sciences,"http://wire0.ises.org/wire/publications/perspec.nsf, 1999.

[2] Queen's University, "Queen's harnesses sun with first solar-electric paneled building," http://qnc.queensu.ca/story_loader.php?id=3ef897043d141, June 24, 2003.

[3]Refocus Weekly, "Most renewables now are cost competitive with combustion sources, says IEA," http://www.sparksdata.co.uk/refocus/fp_showdoc.asp?docid=8300418&accnum=1&topics=, July 30, 2003.

[4]Ibid.

Chapter Six

Innovation is Always Driven by Learning and Education

In Canada we are blessed with a school system, post-secondary education and training that more or less covers our gigantic nation from coast to coast and from south to north.

Because of the size there are bound to be some areas that are covered better than others. The lack of a national policy on education and training is another shortfall that makes us less effective, but the overall situation is very favourable to innovation and development.

How can we improve that effectiveness? How can we motivate ourselves in our daily learning and teaching to optimize our talents and our resources and to utilize neglected opportunities?

In the following paper on "Necessary Steps in Education: Sustaining and Creating a Sustainable Future," I show the various opportunities we have in learning and innovation. Focusing it on the area of renewable energy gives us a good example. But I need to emphasize that the example of our opportunities in learning, education and training in renewables can easily be transferred, altered and used in any other area.

As I have tried to demonstrate with the Scandinavian example, every society has the option to determine where it will go. In Scandinavia a change in attitude and in direction has transformed countries. Within one generation, they have been catapulted from the end of the line to the front and have become world leaders in productivity and innovation.

The world is once again at a turning point, and in Canada we need to decide which turn we want to take. Do we want to endorse and cling to the oil/atomic age and to military dominance like the present U.S. administration, or do we want to embrace a new direction where we seriously consider pathways that will lead us towards a future in tune with the environment and all of our neighbours on this planet?

This paper, presented at the national conference on solar energy, will hopefully inspire all of us to see the wonderful options we have in this and in any other area. The "Canadian Way of Life or Thinking" will surely present us with a sense and direction that will allow us to learn and to innovate in a positive, non-threatening way!

SESCI 2004 CONFERENCE
UNIVERSITY OF WATERLOO
WATERLOO, ONTARIO, CANADA
AUGUST 21–25, 2004

NECESSARY STEPS IN EDUCATION:
CREATING AND SUSTAINING A RENEWABLE FUTURE

Abstract

This paper will look at the steps necessary to achieve broad educational curricula in our elementary, secondary and post-secondary institutions as well as to create the partnerships necessary for successful development of such ideas. It will also consider educational concepts already in place elsewhere, and in what venues education can play a necessary role in assisting with the development and deployment of renewables. For example, the availability of trained technical personnel is a basis for successful deployment of renewable energies. Ontario alone has a shortage of some 1000 engineers and installation and maintenance technicians needed to achieve its target of 10,000 MW by 2010. The moment people are employed in production and installation, this will go up significantly and be in the thousands. Thus, training initiatives need to operate in concert with establishing market and policy incentives.

While institutions can lead the educational agenda for renewable energies, public education for those not within the educational system also must be considered, including continuing to educate our governments and public officials on the absolute necessity for alternative energies to become part of the mainstream. In this respect, industry and providers can assist in forwarding the agenda. But perhaps the most crucial link in the educational continuum is to make renewables education a part of everyday life, both inside and outside of the educational system.

A broad-based commitment, on the part of the public and government, to all fields of alternative energy generation will push the renewables agenda forward. We must continue to consider that it is the holistic view of alternative energies that will provide the most significant benefit to our environment, our businesses and industries, and, perhaps most importantly, our homes. However, we also need to put a strong focus on public education, starting with public awareness and an integration of renewable energies, policies and ideas into educational curricula at all levels.

Introduction

It is clear that the emphasis on any educational momentum in renewable energy must include the idea that everything is related to education in one form or another. Thus, when we discuss the deployment of renewable or alternative energy technologies, education must be part and parcel of those initiatives, and on a wide variety of fronts. It is also true that there are a number of other factors that must be considered, and the most important of these is education surrounding energy conservation. We will not succeed in respecting our environment and ourselves appropriately until we have educated ourselves regarding proper conservation practices and alternative energies. I would suggest that conservation is such an important part of the education process that we should consider it yet another form of alternative energy. At this moment, the provincial government of Ontario is struggling to get sufficient supplies lined up. The situation is so serious that expanding atomic energy production is considered to be one of the key options. We must, before we do that, focus on making conservation—the most exciting, more or less immediately available energy—happen. If we, for example, succeed in conserving 20 percent energy, there would be no need to engage in rushing in to mobilizing atomic energy at a questionable prize or outcome.

At St. Lawrence College we are presently using a prototype approach to research ways of converting high-energy-use buildings into buildings that use energy more efficiently and that use alternate renewable energies. The Cornwall Campus professors and students have embarked on this together. The combination of the learning experience and the savings of energy will give us a double return. We have the ambitious goal to finish the planning of the project during the winter, and we should be able to present the pilot project to the provincial Ministry of Energy. Implemented on a large scale, public buildings alone can save more energy than the planned production expansion into atomic energy at the cost of more than $1 billion. Investing this kind of money could help to convert hundreds of institutions, offices, ministries, city halls, hospitals, etc., within the foreseeable future. This would automatically create new industries with thousands of employees. With 100,000 private solar roofs installed in a similar fashion in Germany, more than 500 megawatts of decentralized solar generation was created at a cost of approximately $2 billion, and more than 10,000 permanent jobs were created. With this $2 billion plus an additional $1 billion of private or corporate capital that was invested into buildings and the equipping of a newly evolving industry, the government spending was easily justified. Considering what it costs to create 10,000 new industrial jobs and the numerous other positive side effects such as the educational aspect for a whole nation, this investment was actually very reasonable and resulted in a high permanent return, in addition to being a big relief to the overburdened environment. Germany's vision helped the solar industry to move forward. One of the results is that the cost per Kilowatt is declining dramatically, a trend that will continue and may even accelerate in the next few years.

Regardless of all the figures, imagine what kind of inspirational, educational and industrial impact actions like this would have in Ontario. Just like when the automotive industry was introduced into Ontario and moved us into a new era, renewable energy can help prepare us for a new era of innovation and learning.

This would be an ideal partnership project between the federal government and the province of Ontario. This is just what happened in Alberta, where wind was promoted in partnership.

The fact that 90 percent of Alberta government buildings and a significant part of the public transportation are going to be fuelled with renewable energy will have a lasting educational impact and promote innovation on an even grander scale.

What we need is an holistic educational approach, from cradle to grave, that includes formal educational practices within our school systems, at all levels, in addition to public education for consumers, for business and industry, and for politicians and government. It is telling that, throughout the Green Power Workshop series hosted by Pollution Probe and the Summerhill Group across the country in 2003-2004, education kept coming up as a key point to push renewable energy forward, and yet there was initially not sufficient space to discuss the applications necessary to make education in this field a national priority. This paper will attempt to introduce some of the key ideas we need to address in order to bring renewable energy education into the mainstream of daily life.

111

Policy Concerns and Challenges

As Canada has no central federal government ministry or agency responsible for education, establishing educational policies regarding alternative energies will have to proceed provincially, which poses some interesting challenges in terms of government buy in, pedagogical issues, and the difficulty of dealing with decentralization. Just as it is difficult to achieve consensus on how best to define, create and deploy green power, as the recent cross-country workshops organized by Pollution Probe and the Summerhill Group have shown, the same challenges present themselves when dealing with setting up a lifelong educational curriculum in these areas. Specific lobbying efforts will be needed to target sympathetic politicians and bureaucrats in the areas that renewable energy typically finds its champions, as well as in the more traditional educational circles. Federal and provincial standards and policies on energy of any kind are also badly needed!

In addition, we will have to continue to emphasize the holistic approach that must be taken. Education in renewable energy is another facet of healthy living, as are proper nutrition and health care. This dimension must not be lost if we are to be successful in creating a lifelong learning "package" for renewable energies and practices.

Leadership: The Time Is Now

In seeking a broad-based commitment to renewable energy education, the support of a number of levels of the population must be sought. In particular, governments must be wooed at all levels in order to encourage appropriate policy creation, the purchasing of green power and the creation of new public initiatives, not only at the policy level but also on the level of public education, whether it be a significant curricula direction or something as focused as workshop groups for interested homeowners.

Next, industry must work together with renewable energy providers in order to "advertise" appropriate messaging to a public who will, hopefully, be hungry for news and innovation.

Providers must work together as much as possible. Speaking with one voice is not something we have accomplished, to this point, in Canada, but I believe that it is changing rapidly.

And, last but not least, the public must be engaged in the dialogue along with all of those who have a vested interest in renewable energy, for it is the public that will gain the most benefit in terms of healthier living, in the long run. Everyone must be encouraged to participate in education and in public awareness campaigns.

Targeting Specific Ages and Groups, from Formal Education to Lifelong Learning

When we talk about public awareness campaigns, we must also be aware that making the leap from knowledge to application is not easy. People avoid change for many reasons, and so the cost of change can be high. This is why it is imperative that early education on renewable energies, in the most holistic of ways, is the foundation on which to build an educational model that will serve us well in the future. In this way, we can look at breaking the educational continuum in Canada down into sections, discussing what might be most appropriate at each level in order to achieve specific outcomes that will ultimately enshrine an awareness for, and appreciation of, renewable energies into everyone's everyday consciousness. For the purposes of this discussion, we will be considering ECE/kindergarten, primary/elementary education through to junior high school, high school, and then programs in colleges and universities. After the more formal notion of educational curricula, we must also discuss the best way to approach public education in the broadest possible sense; for example, who are the interested audiences and what is the best way of reaching them in a timely and efficient manner.

Of primary importance, no matter what level of the population or age group with which we are dealing, is the need to make educational resources commonplace, both easily available and accessible to the community and its visitors. We need to make people understand that the buy in begins with the individual: it all begins with *you!*

Kindergarten/ECE

If we truly want to make a difference in education, we must start with the youngest and most impressionable of our citizens, those who are either in early childhood education programs or in the first years of the elementary school system. If we succeed in making renewable energy a commonplace factor in these young lives, there will be no question as they reach adulthood that they will understand and accept the influence that our energy choices have on nature and thus humankind. Materials will need to be provided that explain, in a way that is simple, understandable and fun, how our environment works, the role of energy in our world, the impact that our choices have on the whole system and the importance of conservation.

Better still, if we can come up with materials and curricula that make it play for our youngest children, they won't understand why their parents and other adults have different thought processes, and in turn they will be a significant influence on the adults around them. Hands-on activities that explain "how things work" will be important to this age group, which is often concerned with taking things apart to understand how it all functions. We need to engage their spirit of exploration and their connection to the physical world.

Primary/Junior High

From the time our young people reach elementary school grades through to the junior high school years, they are already learning much about their place in the world and their importance in it. Curricula at this level will still need to have an element of fun, but it also, in turn, must motivate in a practical way. Hands-on activities will continue to be important, not just from a play perspective but also in ways that children can test and experiment with different aspects of renewable energy. It would be worthwhile, for example, to have small, simple demonstration units of the available technologies so that children can see for themselves how they work. An expanded range of literature on the subject will also be important, contributing to increased technological literacy. And, a program like "Biotech in a Box," which I will discuss in some detail in the high school section, is also useful here.

As with the younger children in kindergarten, it will be important to show how our individual choices have an impact on our environmental systems. In Sudbury, at Science North, there is a wonderful new interactive video/object theatre that hammers home the impact that overuse of fossil-based resources has on our environment. Narrated by sheep in a field (voiced by Rick Mercer, one of Canada's young and very popular comedians), *The Climate Change Show*[5] walks children through how our atmosphere came to be and how our use of electricity and fossil resources jeopardizes our future for everyone, including sheep!

As with Science North's other Object Theatres, The Climate Change Show is a multimedia event designed to use video along with special effects, relevant objects, and lighting changes to appeal to various senses that draw the audience into the experience. Object Theatres have been popular exhibits at Science North, offering high quality education and entertainment to audiences.

The Climate Change Show was conceptualized at the beginning of 2001 to address a serious topic worldwide: global warming. A team of Science North staff began to work to bring to reality their goal of increasing public understanding of the dynamic nature of climate change, revealing the present and future impact of global warming and empowering visitors towards positive action.

One of the challenges in developing this Object Theatre was how best to bring this serious topic forward in a way that navigated the muddy waters of social, economic, cultural and political issues that are associated with global warming and climate change. Thus an animated narrator—a talking sheep—speaks plainly about climate change, while the cartoon character allows the opportunity for humour throughout the presentation. Stunning special effects recreate weather patterns, including a storm effect with wind, rain, thunder and lightning, reinforcing the message being relayed by the show. Such an approach could easily be translated to renewable energies (which are already an integral part of the above show). The broad appeal of this medium is indisputable.

High School

In high school, the curricula we must consider need to be broader, more demanding and overarching. These age groups are not only being educated, but they are also at a point in their lives when they will start considering employment. Given that Canada lags behind the rest of the world in terms of having enough trained people to create and maintain renewable energy installations and networks, informing this age group about potential future work opportunities is critical.

I mentioned "Biotech in a Box" earlier. In the Kingston area, the community-incubated, "Biotech in A Box" program delivers portable biotechnology labs for three school boards located in a wide radius around Kingston, including Trenton, Cornwall and Vankleek Hill. The labs provide students access to the sophisticated biotechnology experiments and techniques that few school boards can afford to provide on their own. The two "boxes" consist of a DNA electrophoresis lab and a polymerase chain reaction lab, each containing equipment, materials and instruments necessary to perform industry standard biotechnology experiments in the classroom.

The program grew out of an innovative partnership between St. Lawrence College, the Kingston Economic Development Corporation's (KEDCO) biotechnology action plan, Queen's University, the local public and Catholic school boards and local biotechnology firms in 1999. "Biotech in a Box" was designed to do something proactive that would benefit our local students and the local economy. We quickly realized that many science teachers embraced the emerging biotechnology disciplines with enthusiasm but felt some frustration that they lacked the means and resources to provide their students a window into this new field.

The "Biotech in a Box" model provides secondary school teachers with a crash course in biotechnology through workshops offered by St. Lawrence College before demonstrating the labs at their high schools. There is still a waiting list for the workshops, another indication of its popularity. The Kingston biotechnology action plan has resulted in the city becoming a recognized bio-cluster in Ontario, and "Biotech in a Box" certainly seems to be a good investment for its future success. This success could certainly be repeated in the area of renewable energy.

To date, seven schools from three school boards have utilized the labs throughout southeastern Ontario. Thirty-one teachers have been trained to deliver the workshops, and more than 230 students have been exposed to the program's experiments. "Biotech in a Box" has allowed students "to consider biotechnology as a career option and to connect with the biotechnology firms in the community," says Barbara Heins, the first teacher to use the labs at her Frontenac Secondary School. Heins believes the labs were helpful for the genetics modules of the grade 11 and 12 biology curricula. But for most the thrill "was the chance to use highly sophisticated equipment not accessible to high school students normally. And it was great fun."[6]

The program will be expanded in 2003 to include the students' perspective and the social component of biotechnology, in order to make students aware of the broad range of career opportunities. As with renewables, there is more to the career side than just science. There is a regulatory side to the industry, and it will need people who understand the legalities of the new technologies. In addition, we'll need to educate people to communicate about the field. This is a great age to give idealistic people a good look at what they might accomplish in the field of renewable energy. This is also a neat way to help students who are undecided and lacking direction to activate a passion and a self-motivation to learn and feel part of a real-life experience.

Colleges and Universities

Perhaps the constituency that requires the least convincing of the importance of teaching more about renewable energy is the college and university sector, but even here there needs to be broader application of knowledge. As it stands today, there are specific departments and faculties that address renewables and their technologies, but what is now needed is an "Applied" function, particularly in general course work, that can create an awareness of the practical aspects that need to be addressed. Post-secondary education has a number of functions here: it can create awareness through community education and outreach; it can create applied research; it can provide education and training; it can grow partnerships and commercialization; and it can help with consulting for governments.

Practically speaking, the availability of trained technical personnel is a basis for successful deployment of renewable energies. For maintenance alone, Ontario has a shortage of some 1000 engineers and technicians needed to achieve its target of 10,000 MW by 2010. For production, installation and marketing/sales, thousands of qualified people are needed to develop our own products. Thus, training initiatives need to operate in concert with establishing market and policy incentives. The background document for Workshop 5 of the Green Power Workshop series strongly recommends that an able work force is needed to support the emerging green power industry in Canada.[7]

For example, St. Lawrence College offers a program in environmental assessment, at the technician level. But this offering could easily be expanded to include a more general, continuing education sort of training that could easily benefit interested members of the general public. It would then gain momentum not only as a field of employment but also as an area for contract training and lifelong learning.

Educational institutions, particularly those closely tied to their communities, such as St. Lawrence College, need to be places where renewables technology can be explained in an open and non-threatening way. Not only are we the venue for training those who will build and maintain the equipment, through our programs in Electrical Engineering Technology, but we are also the venue that can best inform the community.

The Association of Canadian Community Colleges is also paying close attention to these developing trends. They have teamed up with several Canadian renewable energy associations to develop a strategy for renewable energy training. With support from Natural Resources Canada and working with CanWEA, CanSIA, CanBIO and the Earth Energy Society of Canada, ACCC is set to develop curricula for several pilot training courses, initially focusing on wind power, photovoltaic, biomass and heat pumps. ACCC is researching the needs of each sector in order to identify competency gaps that need to be filled by training technical personnel. Moreover, the program aims at the implementation of renewable energy technology pilot projects at colleges, outreach to communities and the general public, and the development of a national strategy for green power training in order to leverage support for setting up new training programs.[8]

At St. Lawrence College, we are committed to a significant number of environmental and alternative energy initiatives. We believe that the best way to effect change is to lead, and that is why our Cornwall campus has a demonstration of a wind turbine in operation. At the Kingston campus, there is some exciting research taking place combining two solar technologies. Creating a cooling effect through the installation of a solar wall underneath the photovoltaic generating panel can increase the power generation efficiency of the active photovoltaic array, and at the same time the extracted heat can be used in exchangers, either in the heating or cooling cycle or for heated fresh air intake.

However, I believe that "Energy House" will be our most important contribution to the community in these areas. Energy House is a public education partnership involving St. Lawrence College of Applied Arts and Technology, the school boards in the Kingston area and the general public. It will be a facility used to make alternative energy concepts and products accessible to everyone in the Kingston area—particularly students. Educating the next generation so they understand and embrace alternative energy is key to the future of our environment. Technology is developing at a very rapid pace and becoming more complex but also more competitive. Energy House will focus on alternative energy concepts and products that individuals can use in their homes and in their work, such as solar heating, heat pumps, photovoltaic systems, energy efficiency in construction and in appliance usage.

St. Lawrence College will create a stand-alone facility to incorporate a number of alternative energy technologies to be used as demonstrators and for applied research. The building will be relatively small and in itself energy self-sufficient. We will likely use a portable type building and will incorporate a solar wall air heating system, solar hot water heating, photovoltaic panels for electricity, energy efficient reconstruction of some wall and roof elements, air or ground source heat pump and the possibility of a small wind turbine and/or a residential fuel cell.

120

At both the college and university levels, there needs to be this sort of introductory direction, regardless of the field in which students are studying. Aspects of the environment and renewable energy could easily become a common credit. Multipurpose courses could then lead to credits in other areas as well; for example, there could certainly be a shared curriculum with medicine and healthy living. In Northern Europe, for example, technical universities have such mandatory courses and it is a part of society. The same can be done here.

In addition to the technical aspects, we must also consider the environment and renewable energy in a philosophical way. How and why do we apply renewable energy technologies? How could we best build our houses? The Canada Mortgage and Housing Corporation, for example has an interesting publication in this area, but it needs to be simplified and made more accessible. All of these things are ideas that could be considered in post-secondary education, along with medicine, law, and business, as well as science and technology. It is for this reason that I would argue that a mandatory half-credit in such an area could contribute enormously to economic development.

Informal Education and Lifelong Learning

Clearly I have touched on a number of these areas earlier on, and you can see how much of our discussion can apply to those who are consumers, interested in access to programs that are of interest to them without necessarily being tied to accreditation. I would like to mention a few types of initiatives that we should consider as being integral to lifelong learning. We need to focus on energy awareness courses for the public and for private sector companies. We need to educate consumers on the appropriate attitudes toward energy use and conservation. We need to work within our communities, setting up common interest groups, encouraging volunteers; perhaps, some could become community energy advisors. We need to work with our communities in terms of advising them how best to secure funding for renewable projects they may be interested in developing. We can provide pre-sentations to those who are interested. We cannot take for granted that the public knows anything about the topics we are discussing. Vision Quest, Canada's largest wind power operator and retailer, has shown that while wind and solar are accepted as "green" energies, for example, hydro and biomass-based genera-tion requires some education before it is accepted as such.[9]

Conclusions

A broad-based commitment, on the part of the public and gov-ernment, to all fields of alternative energy generation will push the renewables agenda forward. We must continue to consider that it is the holistic view of alternative energies that will provide the most significant benefit to our environment, our businesses and industries, and, perhaps most importantly, our homes. However, we also need to put a strong focus on public education, starting with public awareness and an integration of renewable energies, policies and ideas into educational curricula at all levels.

At the last Green Power workshop, education and training were identified as crucial requirements for a comprehensive green power strategy. As the document states, education of the general public is required to increase support for green power in Canada, which in turn will enhance political support for, and reduce local resistance to, green power projects. This can be achieved through various means, starting with public forums, ad campaigns, and also power source disclosure on utility bills. Education of the financial sector, governments and investors is also needed to create a paradigm shift and to create the momentum necessary to move to a more diversified energy economy.[10]

In many ways, all of the ideas discussed indicate a significant need to change our lifestyle, and we are at a point in our history, here in Canada, where we have a unique opportunity to do so. Other countries, such as Germany, Scandinavia, the Netherlands, Spain and Japan, are already showing us the way. We have ignored change so far because we have been blessed with an over-abundance of resources, but the impact on the environment has been significant and detrimental to our way of life. Now is the time to redress that impact by making renewable energies a part of everyday life, and the best way to accomplish this is to make it a part of everyday education and lifelong learning. We need to educate teachers and counsellors to show our students new and better directions. We cannot differentiate between renewables; no one technology is better than others, and they all have their appropriate place as well as strengths and weaknesses. We need to show people the best and most appropriate use for these technologies.

As the Green Power Workshops identified, education should be an integral part of a national strategy on renewable energy.[11] I would also argue that a national policy on education would make such work much easier and more effective.

However, it is the necessity of the holistic view that is most crucial. We must all work together to support each other. In this holistic view, conservation must play a major role, without question, and needs to be treated as a renewable energy all on its own. Thus, changing our lifestyles and attitudes becomes a major part of what we must do; self-education is as important as formal education. The more we do, the better our quality of life becomes!

---

[5] Science North, "Featured Exhibits," http://www.sciencenorth.on.ca/learn/exhibits/index.html July 22, 2004.

[6] Council for Biotechnology Information, "Community-Based Science Programs Demystify Biotechnology," http://www.whybiotech.com/index.asp?id=2403, July 2004.

[7] Martin Tampier, "Background Document for the Green Power Workshop Series: Workshop #5" for Pollution Probe and the Summerhill Group, April 3, 2004, p.123.

[8] Association of Canadian Community Colleges, "ACCC Renewable Energy Program," http://www.accc.ca/english/services/renewable_energy.cfm, July 2004.

[9] Martin Tampier, "Background Document for the Green Power Workshop Series: Workshop #5" for Pollution Probe and the Summerhill Group, April 3, 2004, p. 68.

[10] Martin Tampier, "Background Document for the Green Power Workshop Series: Workshop #5" for Pollution Probe and the Summerhill Group, April 3, 2004, p. 52.

[11] Martin Tampier, "Background Document for the Green Power Workshop Series: Workshop #5" for Pollution Probe and the Summerhill Group, April 3, 2004, p. 97.

Chapter Seven

Creating a Healthy Balance Between Urban and Rural Development

Canada is facing the same challenge as other evolving countries. More and more people are leaving the countryside and moving into the major urban areas. There are many reasons for this, but one of the primary causes is the drastic change in farming methods. Logging, fishing, mining and other rural occupations are also being drastically reduced or eliminated. Some new jobs are created in tourism and service industries that cater to the needs of cottage and vacation country but not enough to make up for the heavy losses in the other areas.

In the past, economic development policies and opportunities often supported the creation of industries in rural areas and directed new immigrants to those same areas. In today's world, with the shift of the entire population away from manual labour to more and more white collar and service-oriented jobs, there doesn't seem much left to do in the countryside. Even farming and industrial jobs mainly involve using high-tech equipment or robots that are replacing the farm and assembly line worker of the past.

Development of any kind is directly dependent on the education and training available, and education and training are primarily available in the cities or larger urban centres. As pointed out under the immigration agenda, we will have to rethink our entire approach to economic development and urban versus rural growth.

Urban and City Planning

The days are over when planning with a lack of foresight went unnoticed. The greater Toronto area is a good example of how things evolve without a well-thought-through, sustainable long-range plan. The GTA (Greater Toronto Area) has reached the stage where infrastructure of every kind is close to collapse or operating at maximum capacity. People accept as normal commuting times of one hour to work and another hour back home, and a large portion of people's resources and energy are completely wasted in travel time. This can easily amount to up to 30 percent of their active time. The entire average transportation or travelling time of the GTA population is slightly below this, but if you set this at 20 percent or two hours daily of the active time, we are talking about more than $100 billion waste of productive time, energy and other resources per year just in the GTA region. As long as we consider human time cheap or worthless and energy costs low, we can ignore this situation, but the moment values change—perhaps when the environment cannot endure any more—it will be economically, emotionally or spiritually unbearable to continue to ignore the effects of a commuter way of life.

We also need to keep in mind that we gradually lose our competitiveness. Waste, regardless where it originates, sooner or later always translates into dollars/productivity lost. Again, the Scandinavian and European example show a refreshing difference, where the majority of jobs are accessible by bicycle or public transportation in under thirty minutes.

To employers in a lot of underdeveloped countries, the short distance to the workplace gives an additional advantage on top of lower wages/benefits and better work ethics. Considering that production techniques and facilities in the future will be equally efficient everywhere, we will need to be more focused on developing new approaches to distances to our workplace and the amount of energy and time used for transportation. We will have to be a lot more innovative when we are creating jobs.

Underdeveloped countries in many areas are not as underdeveloped any more, and they are reaching out for jobs in our own backyard. Many of today's soft industries can be handled from anywhere regardless of location. Thousands of highly skilled and educated software specialists in India and China are already a part of our indirect work force and deliver top quality work at very reasonable prices/wages.

Urban development is only meaningful and sustainable if there is a proper long-term plan in place that ensures sufficient infrastructure, including efficient public transportation.

Small Town/City and Rural Development in Conjunction with Greater Metropolitan Areas

Government should and could encourage development outside the GTA (which includes everything between Barrie, Hamilton Kitchener/Waterloo and Oshawa), GOA (Ottawa), GMA (Montreal), Moncton–Halifax, Winnipeg–Regina/Saskatoon, GCA (Calgary), GEA (Edmonton) and GVA (Vancouver).

There are of course many good examples of smaller centres evolving. London and Windsor are good examples of development outside the GTA. Well-planned development could easily give areas like Belleville, Kingston, Brockville and Cornwall a boost in a way that enables a more efficient and harmonious development of infrastructure, including transportation.

Forty percent of all Canadians live in Ontario, and half of the Ontario population lives in the GTA. Wouldn't it make sense to slowly stop this mushrooming around Toronto and distribute the population more evenly along the corridor between Windsor and Cornwall? When we include GMA (Montreal) in this evaluation, we could be tempted to develop a strong corridor of efficient and innovative transportation infrastructure between Windsor and Quebec City. This area represents more than 50 percent of Canada's population and even a larger share of the entire manufacturing.

Similar opportunities exist in all areas in Canada. There could be other strong corridors, such as Vancouver to Hope; Lethbridge/Calgary to Edmonton; Saskatoon to Regina; Winnipeg to Regina; Sault Ste. Marie to Sudbury, North Bay and Ottawa; Ottawa to Montreal; Saint John, NB to Moncton, NB, Charlottetown, PEI, Truro and Halifax; and many more. By creating many more independent clusters and linking them together with a first-class net of infrastructure including passenger and freight trains, a first-class highway system and other forms of innovative, environmentally-friendly energy and transportation systems, development outside the GTA would be encouraged.

Planning Rural Areas

A change in technology could give us opportunities to reactivate smaller, urban places and even rural areas. The success will depend upon the quality of our planning and our ability to revitalize small, attractive, rural communities.

By creating a string of clusters along certain corridors it is much easier to expand around these in a star-shaped formation that will keep each mini-centre to a manageable size without destroying the surrounding nature/environment.

In the past it was only possible to install larger service-oriented companies in the big centres. Large centres were capable of providing the necessary infrastructure, services and trained, skilled manpower. Nowadays, because a lot of the communication and services move via the Internet, we have other options. Smaller places all across the country, like Moncton, NB, or Kingston, ON, have attracted large call centres with thousands of employees giving service on a regional, national, international or even global basis.

As long as we develop corridors with the entire infrastructure, we can easily attract many companies to interesting smaller urban centres and move large segments of evolving modern industries towards the periphery or in some cases even to more remote areas.

Just as we create attractive ski and resort areas, such as Mount Tremblanc, Whistler or Banff, nothing prevents us from creating attractive rural clusters of various other distinctions. These areas will have no problem attracting certain employers and employees as long as an up-to-date infrastructure is in place.

By creating or maintaining clusters of excellent post-secondary education and training outside the big centres, it will be possible to move some of the growth away from exploding greater centres.

As green or renewable energy will play a much larger role in the future, and these various types of generators like onshore and offshore wind, solar, bio-mass, hydro, geothermal, landfill gas, tidal energy and wave energy are located all across the country, this kind of development can go hand-in-hand with modern economic development.

When we hear the fascinating development in Pincher Creek, Alberta, we can be optimistic about our future. You should listen to the mayor of Pincher Creek. He can tell you a fascinating success story. After depleting the vast natural gas resource within twenty-five years, the growing town of Pincher Creek went into a depressive mood; people left the town and things were getting nasty. All this was turned around in less than three years after a major wind park and related services and industries brought life back into town.

Community colleges in particular can play a major role in helping this kind of innovative development. The 150 Canadian community colleges have campuses in more than 900 communities and can be used as incubators for any kind of development. They can provide training, constantly changing and upgrading the skill set, and thereby help commercialization on a grand scale. The one area where Canada never has led could easily be turned around just like in Scandinavia, if we can get the political will behind this kind of focus.

Canadian universities have been able to compete in research even on a global basis, but unfortunately a small percentage of all patents originate from universities and less than 10 percent of all patents are actually commercialized successfully, which leaves something like a meagre 1 percent of utilized development from universities. This gives us a tremendous untapped potential. Therefore, as a nation we need to move forward and embrace the pairing of the solid research ability at universities and in large companies with the richness of the applied skills and applied research that we find across our vast country in the hands of 150 community colleges. These colleges are in 900 communities, on a daily basis partnering with hundreds of thousands of companies of all sizes and engaged in teaching and learning with more than 500,000 full-time and several million continuing education students. Once we utilize this almost untapped fortune of potential, development and commercialization will take place on a much grander scale.

The Scandinavian example of technology centres, as explained in detail earlier, should inspire and encourage us to create incubators and technology centres in many of the 900 communities mentioned. These communities with college campuses all across our beautiful country have a certain minimum infrastructure. Large-scale innovation and development, as it happened in all of Scandinavia, could and should inspire Canada to follow this kind of grand opportunity.

By embracing this different direction we would stop the influx to the big cities and create a renaissance in rural Canada.

Chapter Eight

Necessary Changes for Creating an Innovation Strategy for Canadian Business

In this chapter I want to paint a vision, a picture of something that could or should change our thinking about business and how we can go about formulating strategies that will take us in a new direction.

Better founded economists can introduce you to the fundamental economical rules we also need to consider when we talk about this. However, I will have the courage to go about it in an unorthodox way.

In order to move forward, it is crucial that we eliminate, or free ourselves, from our greatest weaknesses. This can only be accomplished if we are willing to be honest to ourselves and/or friends and partners without going into a depressive mood. I used the expression *sacred cow* before, and it will possibly pop up a few more times. Change cannot happen without sometimes sacrificing things that are dear to our hearts or to which we have become very accustomed.

Dependence on the U.S. Market

Earlier I mentioned the great dependence upon the U.S. market. Eighty-three percent of all of our exports go to the U.S., which on one hand has given us wealth and great partnerships but on the other hand has automatically made us part of the U.S.A. economic system and situation.

The U.S. has, for many years, lived quite comfortably with a huge imbalance in their foreign trade and an equally big national debt. Although Canada has done the prudent thing in almost always balancing foreign trade and keeping the national debt at a conservative level, by being so much part of the U.S. economy we have lost a large part of our independence. All our efforts and responsible actions will in reality have been in vain, because whenever a major crises hits the U.S. we will automatically be a part of it, whether we wish it or not. Within a few months of any kind of serious U.S. recession we will be equally hard hit, and we will experience the downfall because the U.S. market is practically our only major market.

We may feel quite secure. The U.S., after World War II, has been able with a first-class marketing/image strategy to cover the massive trade imbalance with very substantial foreign investments that constantly pour into the U.S. partly because of higher U.S. interest rates. We must realize, and most people do sense, that the situation since the recession in 1929 has never been as sensitive and critical as it is now.

Only we as Canadians are responsible for being in this dependent relationship that could quickly turn into a major dilemma. We cannot blame the U.S. for buying most of our production from us. Therefore only we can change this, and it cannot be done drastically. The change must take place over time without interrupting present structures. Canada still has, because of its unique situation, the opportunity to reverse this. Internationally we are still considered an independent country, and our image is actually first class.

The change will not be done overnight; however, as a long-range goal it can be implemented realistically within a time frame of twenty to twenty-five years. By reducing the amount of raw material exports, expanding manufacturing and doing all the steps necessary to divert our exports to more countries, we will be able to reverse the figures and gradually reduce the percentage of the product flow to the US. Based on a continued annual growth of approximately 4 percent, we would already reach in a few years the goal just by not increasing exports to the U.S.

As a young man I was involved in exporting food products from Denmark to Germany. I remember clearly that nobody in Denmark in those days believed that it would ever be possible to get away from the dependence on the UK and the German markets. These neighbouring markets took a large portion of all of Denmark's exports. However the tremendous effort to expand to other markets, the gradual growth of production and the diversification in the product range reduced the market share eventually, more or less by itself, without any kind of drastic measures.

The Tort Syndrome

As part of the involuntary integration in the U.S. market and society, we can clearly notice the growing acceptance of legal battles about everything sneaking slowly and gradually into Canada. This may not sound as significant as the dependence on the U.S. market, but we should not kid ourselves; the outcome has a dramatic effect on our behaviour and on the way we live.

Canada was, and to a certain extent still is, a country where security and the respect for other people's property is part of the culture. Gated communities and other symbols of the U.S. way of life are fortunately still the exception. If we as Canadians want to keep our independence and the kind of freedom we are blessed with, we must understand that we will lose all of this if we allow the U.S. legal system slowly to creep into our country and to displace our system. We can only prevent this if we refuse to adopt any of these practices.

Dumbing Down the Federal Government

When I immigrated in the 1960s and negotiated the installation of a small manufacturing plant, I was very pleasantly surprised about the openness, the honesty and the support given by all the provinces with whom I negotiated. When I decided to install the plant in Nova Scotia, it was only because of the circumstances, the availability of certain raw materials, etc.

I clearly remember that I was particularly impressed with the fact that all the bureaucrats I dealt with were very committed, co-operative and willing to take an entrepreneurial position. Many times I could clearly see that the willingness of the administration and the politicians to take a certain risk was part of the spirit of building industry and creating the nation.

It was clear that most policies made some kind of sense and were based on joint experiences and mutual respect between the parties. In spite of all the differences, it appeared also to be possible to get things done in conjunction with the federal and provincial governments. Here also one could sense and experience the co-operative and entrepreneurial spirit. Legalities were also then a normal part of life, but the activities were still driven and controlled by the entrepreneurial issues.

Today you can still find some of this attitude on the provincial levels, but at the federal levels legalities have clearly taken over the agenda. Huge, monstrous bureaucratic structures are creating piles of new policies driven by the need to protect the individuals or departments against any outside interference or objection. Fewer and fewer policies seem to be driven by practical necessities. The change in culture and behaviour is quite stunning and frightening. The tort syndrome is affecting more and more departments, agencies and activities. Not to burden you with too many details, I can give you one of many examples that demonstrate this nicely. Federal agencies, which in the past would have had one employed lawyer, now have twenty or thirty lawyers employed; all these people work at the executive level, and you can imagine how things have changed. Thousands of lawyers have become probably the most influential group of employees within the federal administration and it doesn't surprise us at all that most policy changes are now not driven by factual necessities but more by legalities and protective needs.

A Multicultural Society, One Language and Additional Language Opportunities

Canada is, without any doubt, one of the best countries in the world. One of the reasons for this is our rich cultural background, with a resulting tolerance out of this, and our independence. If we want to protect this status, we will have to prevent harmful developments, particularly at the federal level, that gradually would destroy our values and our richness.

Another very unfortunate development is evolving out of an artificially imposed bilingual status, which more than anything else is dividing our beautiful nation. We all know the history of how this evolved. The French Canadians were for a long time not granted proper rights; however, that does not justify an overreaction of such significance that may have an equally negative impact as the dependence on the U.S. market.

A very critical situation is created unnecessarily when the hiring process at the federal government level prefers language skills over factual skills. Preference to language skills should only be given if other skills are equal. But when the emphasis on the language limits the kind of applicants you can get, it will ultimately create a type of civil servant that does not necessarily represent all of Canada or Canadian interests. When we look at the results of this policy, we can clearly see that this is a very expensive way of governing a united country. This ultimately divides more than unites our big country and could even result in Canada breaking up into two or three blocks. Furthermore, it is ironic but there is not one single indication that the bilingual rule ultimately will prevent Quebec from separating. A separation can, in the long term, only be avoided by showing mutual respect and having enough mutual interests and benefits. This can be seen in many parts of the world, where larger artificial political structure cannot be sustained because of neglecting the above fundamental rules.

Having grown up as part of the Danish minority in the most northerly tip of Germany, I can appreciate what French Canadians have gone through in the past; however, imposing a bilingual status on all of Canada has created some unwanted, costly and very unfortunate side effects, which ultimately could destroy the ability to govern this wonderful country.

Throughout my life as a global entrepreneur, I have learned three languages fluently and developed some good understanding in six other languages. I really benefited greatly from getting to know and understand other cultures but find it very unfortunate and extremely costly to enforce a bilingual state against the will of the majority of Canadians. It could also have been done without making bilingualism mandatory, by giving incentives, by offering a curriculum at school that embraces two extra languages, one by choice and one by necessity of the political or geographical location. This would evolve in a natural way.

Let me show some examples. If you grew up in Quebec, you would learn French and English if you were part of the French culture and one more language of your choice. If you were part of the First Nations, you would learn the native language, French and English. If you grow up in Chinatown, you would learn Chinese, English and French; in a Spanish neighbourhood, Spanish, English and French. For practical and economical reasons, it would be better to have one mutual language with individual rights attached to help keep your background language and culture alive.

As a growing nation we cannot avoid making mistakes. Hopefully we will have the honesty and courage to correct our mistakes as we discover them. It is important to be willing to venture into new areas, to try out unexplored avenues and gain the knowledge and the wisdom that great nations acquire through experience.

Chapter Nine

Bibliocentre: A Model for the Digital Library for the Canadian Future

Digital Learners

The change in the way that information is being delivered and the way Ontarians, for instance, use that information to learn, improve and compete globally, necessitates a *transformation* in the way that they seek, find and evaluate the information they need. Libraries, schools, and academic institutions must partner together to play a central role in this *transformation* to an information literate society, making content, training and services available equalizing access across Ontario and supporting the education, research and government sectors.

Today the attention span of our learners parallels that of top managers. Learning has changed to discovery-based learning which means students are learning to perpetually learn. Today's learners are constantly multiprocessing. They have the ability to navigate through confusing, complex information and to build the connections between knowledge producers and consumers. Technology and in particular the Web has led the change in the way learners learn. Literacy today involves text and also image and screen literacy

Learning Environment

Market profile & environment scan of the entire Canadian market shows incredible shifts underway for educational institutions their libraries & learning resource centres, their learners, their administrations.

Bibliocentre is a unique operation in Canada and the service offerings are extensive when compared with similar service providers. Bibliocentre is renowned for excellence in its core services, Digital Services including foremost the *Colleges Digital Library*, Metadata Production, and E-learning support

Bibliocentre and Ontario's Community Colleges

Established by the Government of Ontario in 1968, the Bibliocentre is a central resource and coordinating agency for Ontario's community colleges, particularly in library and access services. Acting on behalf of the college community, the Bibliocentre facilitates the efficient acquisition, access and distribution of learning resources and develops new technologies to serve colleges, libraries and other information partners. Its prime mandate is to support the college Learning and Resource Centres as a unique cost-saving enterprise that saves colleges money, staffing, computing resources, space, planning services, and the investment needed to research and develop new services in the face of rapid technological change. Colleges and other information centres outside of Ontario are now availing themselves of Bibliocentre services. *Today, let alone tomorrow, indeed presents us with a need to establish tools to support an increasingly universal education and training system with creative, innovative tools and distribution models.*

Supporting the way to research

In 1999, Bibliocentre undertook to offer equitable access to the invaluable online collections of electronic journals and abstracts throughout the twenty-five very diverse Colleges of Applied Arts and Technology (CAAT) in Ontario. The colleges varied widely in their means (and still do); among them are some of the smallest as well as the largest colleges in Canada. Certain aggregated online journals were already provided by some colleges while virtually none were offered by others.

Bibliocentre undertook to consolidate purchase, support and network distribution of core collections from two large vendors (EBSCO and ProQuest) which would be agreed-upon by the colleges via their Users Advisory Group, the invaluable link between the power of a consortium and its members. Bibliocentre established a "Development Fund", "money at the centre" which was provided from its own revenues. This resource established the Colleges Digital Library which provided a consistent, broad array of offerings from the electronic journal distributors.

Subsequently, in a landmark cost-effectiveness study commissioned in 1998, it was clearly demonstrated how the consortium model not only reduces the need for repetitive labour and intellectual review, but also offers the best model for obtaining an optimal pricing and distribution of valuable services such as online journals, centralized access and support. At the time, it was found that the Bibliocentre's overall savings and value to the community colleges was in the order of $5.34 million annually. This figure represents benefit over cost. A strong component of this telling return on investment of $1.87 for every dollar invested was the College's Digital Library. At the time, Bibliocentre also purchased, catalogued and processed some 55,000 items including books, CD-ROMs and learning kits and provided and maintained the growing online union catalogue for the colleges.

What are the salient features of the College's Digital Library that have made it so valuable to students and of such value to the colleges? Some of the consolidated service features:

- One-stop shopping for electronic resources from a long list of vendors and publishers

College libraries contact CDL with requests for quotes and

trials of new products. CDL liaises with the vendors, sets up trials, coordinates individual or group pricing, and vets and signs contracts (i.e. assumes the liability) on behalf of the libraries.

- First-line technical support and troubleshooting

Products purchased through the Bibliocentre get *free* first-line technical support from CDL. College libraries report a problem to CDL Electronic Resources Librarian who works to resolve it. If the problem cannot be resolved at CDL, CDL liaises with the vendor's technical support to find a solution.

- Remote access service

CDL provides a secure, authenticated remote access service for the libraries at a very nominal cost ($240 per college per year), so that users can access electronic resources from home.

- Centralized invoicing

CDL provides one-stop invoicing for the libraries and for the vendors. The various vendors bill CDL/Bibliocentre throughout the year, and CDL produces two consolidated invoices for each college library (one in the Spring, the other in the Fall). In addition, CDL sends a summary statement for the full year to each college so that the libraries have the figures for budgeting and review the following year.

- Local loading of content

CDL maintains servers for loading electronic content for access by the colleges. This service is free to the colleges and saves them the cost of purchasing, operating and maintaining an in-house server.

- Centralized training and facilities

CDL coordinates with the suppliers training sessions for the colleges. Sessions may be held at the Bibliocentre's North York office or in colleges across the province.

- Integration of electronic resources with the union catalogue

CDL integrates library records for electronic resources into the union catalogue, all the while ensuring that there are no copyright infringements. CDL also archives these records and stores them in a secure server so that individual college libraries may download them into their local systems.

- Representation on committees and groups

CDL represents the Ontario colleges in provincial, national, and international consortia and advocacy groups such as COOL (Consortium of Ontario Libraries), OLRN (Ontario Learning Resources for Nursing), Consortia Canada and ICOLC (International Coalition of Library Consortia).

- Leadership for college libraries

The CDL leads projects for the colleges such as creating an e-book collection, Virtual Reference service, and the cataloguing and delivery of electronic government documents.

- Responsive to the college libraries

The CDL Electronic Resources Librarian provides financial and technical updates to the Bibliocentre board (User Advisory Group) which meets quarterly. In addition, the Executive Director of the Bibliocentre brings forward to the UAG further information on the strategic direction and further service enhancements possible regarding the CDL. The UAG is then able to vote on both the specific initiatives as well as the strategic plan for the CDL. The CDL is therefore tailored to fit the College's actual needs.

Colleges Digital Library Today

Is the project still returning value? In September 2003, the Bibliocentre commissioned a second cost-effectiveness study (prepared by Kathryn Cestnick, The Advisors Group) which found some extraordinary results. With virtually no additional staff but with freshly developed and unique bibliographic and systems processes and tools (and fine-tuned methods of delivery), the Bibliocentre was now found to be saving the CAAT college system $10.1 million annually. The organization was not only meticulously cataloguing and shipping substantially more materials (up to some 75,000 fully processed items were shipped out of its loading dock in the previous year), but the CDL was saving the colleges $2,270,000 in overall purchase power and staff. This figure represents an increase of almost 90% in value to the post-secondary education system in just five years. It also represents a telling example of how a universally-oriented educational system—here the Ontario colleges—can prove more adept and open to change than some of the most rigorously intellectual centres of education. You might recall Darwin's statement about those most responsive to change.

Colleges supporting the model for a "universal" Ontario Digital Library

After much vision and effort, the infrastructure and content for the Ontario Colleges Digital Library is in place. New services and products are being examined to increase its value in the coming years. At the moment, on the broader, province-wide front, the provision of digital resources is less structured and more varied. There is simply no equity. Public libraries offer virtually no electronic resources. Schools have even less. The universities with their greater funding and endowments have a more divergent set of online resources available throughout the members of the Ontario Council of University Libraries. The University of Toronto can provide its students with just about anything published online. Small institutions do with less. The universities' purchasing is strong in the applied health areas through collaborative efforts such as the Coalition of Ontario Health Libraries, but these prove the wonderful exception and there is notably less 'universal' availability of resources in the social sciences, for instance.

The colleges' successful model should be a reliable indicator that the other publicly funded library and information services can obtain similar results. And there is great movement underway for an innovative solution to lifelong access, lifelong learning. The Ontario Digital Library is a proposed agreement among Ontario's 6,500 college, university, school and public libraries which have come together for the first time. It will introduce a new generation of services that meet people's changing information needs. The project will leverage existing library capacity and infrastructure to provide resources and expertise that support all Ontario citizens as they move through their lives.

What drives this innovative, cross-Ministry initiative? The Ontario Digital Library is being driven by the both the message and the evidence. People are being urged to become life-long learners, to re-skill, to continuously keep ahead of the constant change in their fields for both economic and social reasons ... and they need the tools to do so. At the same time, changes to the information fabric of our society which supports every aspect of our lives—cradle to grave—in education, higher education and even recreation are increasingly beyond the informed reach of any one area, be it public libraries, our schools, post-secondary sources or even any one level of government.

Governments must realize that the foundation of a successful, prosperous society, their jurisdiction, is more than just bricks and mortar. It is the information fabric that closely knits the social fabric and helps citizens move forward. Government itself knows its connection to its citizenry is not found solely on the roads and highways, but in the informed access to information both shared and widely available. The ODL is an initiative worthy of full support of the citizenry and its responsible government.

Toronto, 11 October, 2001

Chapter Ten

Apprenticeship Training the Traditional Way and Apprenticeship Training Embedded in a Co-op Diploma

Developing a Federal/Provincial Policy and Standard for a More Integrated Universal Education and Training System

If we imagine that a national partnership between universities and colleges, small and large companies, provincial and federal governments develops to its true potential, we will be heading towards a real renaissance of opportunities. Another equally or more important part of this puzzle is a seamless integration of all levels of education. It starts with the primary and secondary system of education that is preparing students according to their talents, desires and goals. Presently the majority of our students have the wrong level of education. Our society, including parents, teachers and high school counsellors, direct them all to university regardless of whether or not they are academically inclined.

We all know the devastating result. No more than 20 to 25 percent of the entire secondary school population will ever finish university. A similar number of students will graduate from college. What happens to the remaining 50 percent who end up without any credentials or formal post-secondary education? This is the saddest side of our well-meaning society. Twenty-five percent of the total number are high school "dropouts." The remaining 25 percent will in most cases have very little opportunity to ever go far beyond the high school diploma. If they get any additional credentials, they will usually only be recognized if they are university degrees or college diplomas. But even college diplomas or apprenticeship certificates are largely considered inferior to anything from university. Therefore only around 25 percent of our population end up with some kind of truly accepted credentials, 25 percent with the somewhat less respected college credentials, and 50 percent without anything that is recognized.

Again, when we compare this system with most systems in place in Europe or specifically in Scandinavia or Germany, we quickly detect a major difference. In Europe we end up with around 30 to 40 percent high school graduates, 40 to 50 percent middle school graduates and approximately 10 to 20 percent public and special school graduates. Because of the more diversified post-secondary process, a high percentage of apprentices and additional pathways within a totally integrated system, the outcome is reversed: more than 60 percent of the population end up with recognized credentials from universities, colleges and trades schools, in some regions as high as 80 percent.

What do we learn from this? We can see clearly that the high level of university graduates only influence the final outcome marginally. Productivity and effectiveness goes up through a broad based education and training. In reality, there are only so many jobs where an academic education is needed; there are many more jobs where the education of basic skills and training is a better foundation. We can therefore conclude that we must improve our ability to create more diversified pathways starting early on, around grade seven or eight, to ensure the best possible training and education for more than just 50 percent of our students. One thing that will strongly support this claim is the fact that a substantial percentage of college students come from university. Some are, of course, dropouts, but many do have degrees or even master's degrees. In order for them to find employment, they end up at college. These people are going through the agony of several studies, and they end up losing valuable time, in most cases years, of their most productive period.

I realize that it will take a great deal of courage, honesty and commitment to redirect our efforts. But with the kind of financial support that most of our provincial governments are giving grade school education, it will only take a refocusing and re-allocation of activities and funds. It will not take more funding than the present system. If and when we create pathways for all students, the possibilities will dramatically increase and a lot of duplication will be prevented.

The commitment by the newly elected Dalton McGuinty government to keep students in school until the age of eighteen can give a real boost to the diversification and multi-pathway concept. However, without an innovative plan for helping less-motivated students, this very positive commitment could easily backfire and burden the entire system. It will only be beneficial if the students can be motivated to engage in meaningful learning and training. The Ontario Youth Apprenticeship Program is one excellent example of what can be done. This program (OYAP) has in the last few years given a real boost to the preparation of apprenticeships. The dramatic increase in apprenticeships in a city like Kingston can give hope to the general development. One of the many impressive projects has been the building of more than thirty-eight good quality houses by the high school students, supervised only by their own pre-apprenticeship trade teachers.

Under a system of multi-pathways, students who are now just sitting their way through high school and bringing down average classroom performance would not hinder students who are academically strong. These academic students will be able to do much better and be more effective. Therefore their ability to succeed at university or college will increase dramatically. The other group of students, who are "sitting their way" through high school, will equally benefit from being able to do things they are more inclined to do. They will also find their direction sooner and experience how gratifying skills training can be and how wonderful it is to be somebody who does something meaningful instead of hanging around.

Apprenticeship Training the Traditional Way and Apprenticeship Training Embedded in a Co-op Diploma

Earlier in the book I mentioned how we succeeded in getting $88 million real new funding for apprenticeships from the Mike Harris government. This innovative approach to apprenticeships, presented by SLC and championed by Hon. Bob Runciman and Hon. Dianne Cunningham, received within a few months broad-based support by the Ministry of Training Colleges and Universities. It led to my own personal appointment to the steering committee of reforming apprenticeships, together with Richard Johnston, president of Centennial College, and under the chairmanship of ADM Bill Forward. Luckily we succeeded early on in getting strong support from the Deputy Minister Kevin Costante, followed by the support of the COP Council of Presidents of ACAATO, Association of Colleges of Applied Arts Ontario.

The following documentation shows you the sequence of the development and the events. Below that is an innovative outcome, a description of how apprenticeships can be delivered in a modern and more acceptable form for Canadian society.

It is clear that the need to increase basic skills training and apprenticeships must continue to embrace the traditional way with a direct learning and training partnership between the employer, the employee (apprentice), the ministry and the college, to the largest possible extent. As long as we can find employers and apprentices for this model (and this can be enhanced through tax credits), it is still one of the best ways of delivering apprenticeships.

In addition to the traditional method, apprentices can be trained in a co-op diploma model. This model must be built slowly and carefully, avoiding any unnecessary mistakes and any kind of confrontation with the traditional system, including all excellent trade union and college programs.

MEDIA RELEASE

Eastern Ontario Jumps at Harris' Offer to "Seize Tomorrow's Opportunities"

Just last week Ontario Premier Mike Harris unveiled his party's new slogan, "Seizing Tomorrow's Opportunities." Eastern Ontario has responded quickly to this vision in the form of a proposal that would see a number of education, training and labour organizations work in concert with municipalities to create Trades Skills Training Centres (TSTC).

Government and industry are forecasting significant shortages of skilled tradespeople. Failure to proactively address these shortages will interfere dramatically with the ability of the business community to succeed and create new wealth and prosperity throughout the province.

St. Lawrence College would take the lead in the development of a variety of skilled-trades programs. The new programs, backed by local school boards, industry groups and city councils, would provide students with a split of theoretical studies and hands-on experience and would serve to address the current and projected skill shortages in Ontario.

"Industries are crying for skilled people, and we would like to be in a position to deliver them," says college president Volker Thomsen. "Our goal is to create a culture where people recognize that being a skilled tradesperson carries with it as much prestige as any other profession. Parents, teachers and students often have misconceptions about these occupations, maintaining an image of trades as they were thirty or forty years ago. Trades persons today are bright, well-educated, well-trained people. We need to promote these careers, which can be very lucrative and rewarding."

Eastern Ontario has pulled together to develop a proposal that goes hand-in-hand with the premier's vision. The next step is to secure provincial support for the St. Lawrence training model and make the creation of Trades Skills Training Centres in Brockville, Cornwall and Kingston a reality.

St. Lawrence College

TRADES SKILLS TRAINING CENTRES
PROPOSAL

The Challenges

"The supply of skilled labour is so tight in the Canadian construction industry that developers say they may have to cancel or postpone key projects." This is according to a December 5 Canadian Press release.

Availability of technicians and other skilled workers is so far below the current demand in Eastern Ontario, a region where unemployment levels are an ongoing concern, that in a recent article on the subject in the Cornwall Seaway News, Denis Thibault's headline read, "Help. The Sky is Falling...The Sky is Falling..."

Many tradespeople are at or near retirement age and will no longer be available to do the work required or to act as mentors in the training of new apprentices. The Ministry of Training Colleges and Universities has reported that there are recognized shortages, particularly in occupations such as electrician, millwright, instrumentation technician and automotive technician.

In the Trades Training Survey prepared for Eastern Ontario Training Board in November, 2000, employers of small-, medium- and large-sized enterprises were queried about training/ apprenticeship needs. They identified needs in several trades areas: Mechanic, Millwright, Drafting, Electronic Test Technician, Industrial Electronic Instrumental, Mig Welding, Welder/ Fitter/ Fabricator, Steam Fitter and Plumber.

In addition to the current and projected shortages, the skilled trades face another challenge: image. Parents, educators and students are too often focused on a very narrow range of "respectable" career options. They maintain an image of careers as they were thirty or forty years ago. Trades persons today are bright, well-educated, well-trained people, who can have very lucrative and rewarding careers. This message needs to be communicated more effectively.

The Opportunity

St. Lawrence College will seize the opportunity to address these challenges through creation of Trades Skills Training Centres (TSTC) in Brockville, Cornwall and Kingston. The college will take the lead on the initiative, which is being supported by Eastern Ontario school boards, city councils and labour organizations. The project will see these groups work together in a true regional partnership. The Centre's activities will involve a number of phases.

Phase 1 will focus on the initial selection of students in secondary schools. Students who have been selected by guidance counsellors, regardless of current skill levels, as having an interest in the trades, will be encouraged to explore what the Centres have to offer. Part of this phase will be a communications plan to bolster the images of trades and to inspire students to pursue a career in this area.

Phase 2 will incorporate Trades Demonstration Days at the Centre. These events will be held on a regular basis, and will feature tradespersons from a wide variety of areas demonstrating their skills and using operating equipment. Trades Demonstration Days will include guest speakers and presentations and will also serve to enhance the image of trades.

Phase 3 will involve exposure to the theoretical training in the trades areas that take place at St. Lawrence College.

Phase 4 will represent site orientation sessions, in which the students will have an opportunity to gain valuable hands-on experience in the field and round out their knowledge and skills base.

St Lawrence plans to develop additional stand-alone programs, which would include customized modules tailored to meet the needs of specific trades occupations.

This proposal is unique in that it would address two components of the projected skill shortage. It would provide students with an opportunity to learn and the incentive to pursue careers in the trades. In addition, the nature of the partnership being formed in support of this project would lend itself to some new concepts such as the possibility of opening our doors to fee-paying, non industry sponsors applicants, and even a model that might see the centres play a significant role in the delivery of trades skills for secondary schools.

The Catalyst

In light of the premier's recent announcement regarding his vision for the future and his commitment to keeping Ontario competitive, we feel that the timing for this particular project is perfect.

Our Eastern Ontario partners, led by St. Lawrence College, are indeed prepared to seize "tomorrow's opportunities" through the development of this unique proposal, and we remain committed to continued improvement in the quality of life and economic prosperity of the region.

The Partners

As noted previously, the proposed Centres for Skills Trades would represent a partnership among municipalities, local school boards, labour organizations and St. Lawrence College.
St. Lawrence College has campuses in Brockville, Cornwall and Kingston and currently serves over 5,000 full-time students and over 20,000 part-time students. Programs include offerings in the

schools of Engineering Technology and Trades, Business Health Science, and Human Studies.

St. Lawrence College graduates are very successful in getting jobs, with nine out of ten working within six months of graduation. The college has also been very successful in the Ministry of Training, Colleges and Universities Key Performance Indicators. Students, graduates and employers of graduates all report high levels of satisfaction.

St. Lawrence College is already a moving force promoting trades in Eastern Ontario. The College has existing trades training facilities and has had specific involvement in training programs for Carpenters, Electricians, Esthetics, Hairstylists, General Machinists, Industrial Mechanics (Millwright), Motor Vehicle Techniques, and Plumbers.

In addition, the college recently appointed its first trades consultant. Russ Phin has had almost forty years experience in the Kingston area in Apprenticeship Training under the Ministry of Training, Colleges and Universities. Mr. Phin has an impressive and extensive background in this area and will play a key role in the development of the Trades Skills Training Centres.

In Summary

In order for Eastern Ontario to "seize tomorrow's opportunity" of addressing challenges currently facing us in the trades area, we need the Government of Ontario to come on board as a partner, in recognition that investing in this vision of the future will make a real ongoing difference to the quality of human resources and economic development of the region.

We invite your participation in the discussion and implementation measures required to make the creation of the Trades Skills Training Centre (TSTC) a reality.

SUMMARY: HOW TO MOVE FORWARD ON THE BASIC SKILLS AND TRADE SKILLS FRONT

To ensure success for the Innovation and Learning agenda, Canada, as a whole, must focus on basic skills and trades skills and ensure that our young people are encouraged and offered the opportunity to build an attractive career, packaged and presented in an appealing way.

The hundreds of thousands of trades people who immigrated to Canada primarily in the first sixty years of the past century are already retired or retiring. They helped to a large extent to build the wonderful and successful modern industrial country we live in.

We want to continue to build on this and on the foundation created by all of our ancestors. With our own human resources, it is possible to create a modern Canadian version of apprenticeships superior to any past or European model. We cannot count on sufficient future immigrants with these types of skills and would be well advised to promote an adapted model that fits into this day and age and addresses our future needs.

It is encouraging that most of the provincial governments, including Dalton McGuinty's Liberals in Ontario, are embracing this concept and that Paul Martin's vision for Canada's future includes a strong investment in basic skills training and learning in general.

It is also very encouraging that apprenticeships in Ontario in the 2004-5 budget are getting an additional boost that will allow for an increase from 19,000 to 27,000 apprentices and a strong introduction of the new apprenticeship co-op diploma and with credits for employers.

All of this should help to formulate a national vision on training and education. Only through strong collaboration will we be able to prepare our nation appropriately for future success and prosperity.

In order for Eastern Ontario to "seize tomorrow's opportunity" of addressing challenges currently facing us in the trades area, we need the Government of Ontario to come on board as a partner, in recognition that investing in this vision of the future will make a real ongoing difference to the quality of human resources and economic development of the region.

We invite your participation in the debate and implementation of measures required to make the creation of the Trades Sills Training Centre (TSTC) a reality.

The Concept:

In order to create winning choices for Ontario's learners and seize tomorrow's opportunities today, Ontario needs an open-ended, flexible training system capable of addressing current and futures needs for skilled trades people.

The creation of Trades Skills Centres in Brockville, Cornwall and Kingston will provide an opportunity to develop a range of programming that allows the learner to enter the workforce and then re-enter training as need and life circumstances require. The diagram that follows illustrates how the system works.

YEAR 1

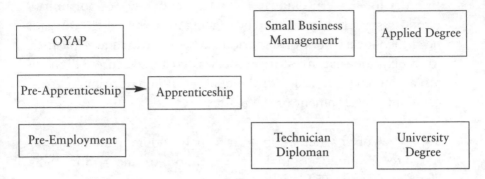

The Trades Skills Centres provide a unique opportunity to:

- Establish a collaborative process between school boards, the college, local government, trades, industry and labour organizations to work on the development of the Centres.

- Create a seamless curriculum for trades training to meet the needs of learners from high school through to and including post Certificate of Qualification Skills updating.

- Develop and deliver customized programs for industry.

- Provide multiple points of entry and exit.

- Implement articulated model credential recognition.

- Create a pool of available skilled workers.

Trades Skills Training Centres can provide trades-focused, multi-level opportunities ranging from introducing middle school students to the trades as a potential career choice to providing post Certificate of Qualification skills to Ontario's workers.

A Model for Learning:

Adults have unique learning needs. In Trades Skills Centres, student achievement is structured around answering the question "What will the learner be able to do?" (learning outcome).

Theory and practice are integrated in all aspects of the program.

Programming at the Centres will include entry level training, apprenticeship training and technician level training. Although each level is independent and can lead directly to the work force, each level will be articulated to the fullest extent possible in order to allow learners a seamless transition if they choose to acquire further training.

Entry-Level Programs

Entry Level training includes pre-employment and pre-apprenticeship programs and provides an opportunity to link with area high schools for Ontario Youth Apprenticeship Programs (OYAP). It also provides an opportunity to link to the Ontario government's Literacy and Basic Skills program, particularly the OBS IV component. Entry-level programs provide students with basic theoretical and practical knowledge in various trades sectors. They allow students to acquire the entry-level skills that employers expect from new workers. Trades Skills Centres will provide pre-employment and pre-apprenticeship programs targeted at construction, electrical, tourism, industrial and mechanical trades.

Apprenticeship

Apprentices are required to attend from four to ten weeks technical training courses in each period of apprenticeship. Before, during and after the in-school training, apprentices work on-the-job to complete the practical requirements of their apprenticeship. Once an apprentice has completed the in-school requirements and the necessary on-the-job training hours, s/he is eligible to write the certificate of qualification examination. Apprenticeship programs include Carpenter, Construction and Maintenance Electrician, Industrial Electrician, Hairstylist, General Machinist, Industrial Mechanic (Millwright), and Plumber.

Technical Programs

Technician programs are two-year diploma programs that enable graduates to work in a variety of different environments. St Lawrence College is committed to developing a Small Business Management Trades program for those who have completed the in-school portion of an apprenticeship program. One year of academic recognition will be granted for the in-school apprenticeship training, while the remaining year will focus on the skills necessary for tradespersons to successfully own and operate a trades-based business. The table below shows the proposed programming in the Trades Skills Centres.

Entry Level Training	Apprenticeship	Technician program
Construction Techniques	Carpenter Industrial Woodworker Cabinetmaker Acoustical Ceiling & Drywall Installer Painter & Decorator Floor Covering /Tile Setter	Small Business Management Trades Interior Design Construction Technician Civil Technician
Mechanical Construction Techniques	Plumbing/Steam Fitting Refrigeration/ Air Conditioning Sheet Metal Worker Gas Fitter	Mechanical Engineering Technician Small Business Management Trades
Industrial Mechanics Techniques	General Machinist Tool & Die Maker Industrial Maintenance Mechanic / Millwright Automotive Service Technician	Small Business Management-Trades Mechanical Engineering Technician Automotive Service Technology CNC Machinist Technician Industrial Technician
Electrical / Electronics Techniques	Construction & Maintenance Electrician Industrial Electrician Instrumentation Mechanic	Small Business Management —Trades Instrumentation Technician Computer Automated Control Technician
Tourism/Hospitality Techniques	Cook Baker	Hotel & Restaurant Management Small Business Management-Trades
Esthetician	Hairstylist	Small Business Management-Trades

The development of Trades Skills Centres in Brockville, Cornwall, and Kingston will do much to help learners in Eastern Ontario "seize tomorrow's opportunities." St. Lawrence College staff is eager to partner with others to create Trades Skills Centres to meet the needs of the region and the province.

Chapter Eleven

Developing a Humane Policy on Immigration

It is very important that the federal government, in conjunction with the provinces, without further delay revises the immigration policy to reflect our need to attract the best and most capable, skilled immigrants and international students and to enable our students to go for an educational exchange in any country of their choice. I was informed during a conversation with the Swedish ambassador to Canada that the Swedish government encourages students to study abroad, and if there are no exchange programs available the government pays the students for out-of-country studies the equivalent of what it would cost to study in Sweden. No wonder tiny Sweden is an intellectual and industrial giant and that it ranks among the first three countries in competitiveness and productivity.

If we in Canada want to stay independent and succeed on the international market, we must do the same as the U.S.A., the EU, Japan, China and other major players are doing. We must make ourselves ready and fit to compete globally and participate in every major market as a significant player. That within a short few years we have fallen from ninth to sixteenth rank in competitiveness must encourage us even more to address our weaknesses and identify our opportunities. The Scandinavian success story speaks for itself and must inspire us to aim for a similar placement.

To achieve this with the least investment and greatest effectiveness, our continued growth must be secured by strategies that support this goal. We know that one of the strategies we must work on is the growth of our population, which is based mainly on immigration.

The Importance of National Policy on Education and Training being Linked to Revised Policy on Immigration

It is quite apparent that immigration policies or practices used during the last number of years have been more counter-productive than helpful. The many strange experiences that immigrants have gone through in the last decade could fill books. I do not want to dwell on the hardships that were created but want to emphasize that immigration in the early days, for example after World War II, was much more focused on the real needs and allowed for a better mix of skill sets according to market demand. When the offices of Manpower and Immigration were under one roof, there was at least some form of synchronizing the real needs with actual immigration. When the Department of Immigration Canada was separated, one might have expected that a stronger focus would create a more efficient system. Unfortunately the opposite has evolved.

The perception in our society about trades and basic skills is that this is an area people only select as a last resort if their academic performance does not permit them to enter university. The school system is not encouraging young people to target jobs that involve any kind of manual labour. Apprenticeships demand a good academic level in certain areas like math, physics, etc., and the entry requirements have been elevated to a high school diploma with good skills in the mentioned areas of science. People with this type of skill set are high in demand in several academic areas and therefore are encouraged to go to onto a post-secondary education, rather than into trades.

The overall outcome is even more depressing. The separated Ministry of Immigration created high academic entry levels (master's degree). The result was that badly needed tradespeople and other people with basic skills no longer entered the flow of immigrants. Most European tradespeople are trained after completing a middle school education with strong supporting elements like math skills, etc. Middle school as a formal basic education does not fit into today's picture of a Canadian education, even if the ten-year focused preparation for most practical jobs is probably a better preparation than our high school diploma.

As a result of today's immigration policy, we are now encountering a flow of highly qualified, or in many cases overqualified, academics who, because of various reasons, have great difficulties in entering the workforce. In many cases these academics end up working as dishwashers or taxi drivers. Because of this unhappy state, if they can manage financially, they usually enrol in new full-time studies over some years and sometimes over many years. This results in ironic situations.

We have one acquaintance who trained as a MD and as a musician in China. When he immigrated he hoped that he would be able to confirm his MD credentials by certain examinations or upgrading. In spite of great efforts in several provinces and over a period of more than a year, he did not succeed in finding a pathway. He was then encouraged to go into social studies with the goal of helping people with disabilities. Four years later, upon reaching the mature age of forty-four, he graduated with honours. He was relieved to finally have some recognized Canadian credentials and started to apply for work throughout all of Ontario but again without success. He has, with the help of his wife who began to work in Regina shortly after they immigrated, found two part-time jobs, one based on his social studies and another as part-time teacher in music. When we reflect on what has happened in this couple's life, we realize that the effect of Canadian immigration rules and policies is often cruel and inhumane. Neither partner was able to work in the area of their expertise. They then had to separate for more than five years.

One of the partners earned a livelihood and enabled the other to study for a new career. After all of this effort and sacrifice they still ended up in a situation where most of their investment into certain studies did not lead to employment in that field. Luckily they can now live together and make a living. This would have been possible many years earlier if we had the kind of practical immigration rules as in earlier years and realistic pathways to get credentials ratified. This couple would never have decided to immigrate to Canada if they had known the obstacles, and, furthermore, they would not have wasted the most productive years of their lives. If they had gone back to China they would have been much better off. But this was not really an option for them. According to Chinese customs they would have lost face, which based on Chinese philosophy is the most a person can lose.

There are presently enough highly qualified foreign-trained unemployed or otherwise employed medical doctors in Canada to easily overcome the shortage of family physicians in our country. The same, or a similar bureaucratic mismanagement, prevents them from getting their credentials recognized or their skill set upgraded. There are many similarly unfortunate examples. As president of SLC I meet students daily who have all kinds of top credentials, immigrants and non immigrants, who after a long odyssey very often end up going for a basis skill in order to become employable.

If a qualified tradesperson or entrepreneur wants to immigrate to Canada right now, even with the intention and proof that they are planning to invest substantial amounts into their own company, in areas where we are encountering shortages, it can take up to five years to succeed, or it may never happen.

Student exchanges and recruiting international students for periods longer than five months as well as professors and scientists for longer exchanges are some of the many areas in which the present immigration policy hinders more than helps and is almost counterproductive.

Why is it so Important to have a Well Developed International Student, Teacher or Knowledge Exchange?

Student exchanges and knowledge exchanges are some of the few vehicles available that foster social, economical and cultural developments between continents, countries and even provinces.

The outrageously high percentage (83 percent) of our exports going to the U.S.A. developed partly because of the geographical proximity and partly because of a lack of political leadership and will to change things. This has resulted in the fading away of economic and cultural ties to European countries and other markets outside the U.S.A. and Asia.

It is certainly neither for the lack of resources nor for the lack of talented people. The originally strong ties to Europe and the rest of the world, which were based on the traditional background of immigrants to Canada, are gradually dying. This has driven us into an unacceptable level of dependence on the U.S.A. and at the same time deprived us of a much larger international exchange of trade and knowledge.

As an example, Canada is as a nation only investing $1.6 million annually in recruiting international students, professors and scientists. Other countries are doing much better. The UK invests $900 million, the U.S.A. $380 million, Germany $320 million, and even Australia, with $14 million, is doing much better.

Because of a direct personal and professional link to the Secretary General of the German DAAD, we have access to the overall German data. The competitive analysis shows $320 million spent annually by DAAD, which actually is correct. They are handling 75,000 exchanges annually (50 percent foreign students in Germany and 50 percent German students abroad). However it does not show another similar amount spent by other German government agencies like the Carl Duisberg Foundation and Alexander von Humboldt Foundation, who handle the international training and exchanges of top scientists respectively. Therefore the overall commitment is similar to the significant UK engagement.

International Recruiting: Competitive Analysis

Competitor Countries	Policies and Organisations	Resources Allocated	Strategies for Recruiting	Immigration issues
Australia	National policy, run by Australia Education International (AEI) and one private NFP, IDP Education Australia	**C$ 14 million annually**, $ 8 million directly from the government. 10 Overseas offices. IDP Australia annual turnover C$ 80 million and 68 offices in 35 countries	Several options in place to attract skilled workers	Immigration policy changes that allow international students who graduate from Australian institutions to remain under a number of different visa categories.
New Zealand	National Policy run by New Zealand International Education Marketing Network (NZIEM)	**C$ 3 million over 3 years**, 9 overseas offices	Immigration regulations changed to include a Talent Visa" and Skills Shortage work permit	International students who graduate from NZ institutions and who qualify under the Talent Visa/Work Skills Shortage can apply from permanent residency
Germany	National policy run by German Academic Exchange Service (DAAD)	**C$ 320 million annually**, $\frac{1}{2}$ for foreign students studying in Germany and $\frac{1}{2}$ for German students studying abroad. 14 full service and 30 representative offices abroad	Education virtually free, even to international students.	International students with IT degrees from German institutions gain immediate access to work and residency permits, others with special qualifications find it easier to obtain residence status depending on labour shortages

France	National policy priority run by Agence EduFrance	Numbers not available; 40 education counselling offices abroad in diplomatic missions, etc.	Education very inexpensive.	International students can apply for permanent residency after living in France for three years, must meet criteria including job skills.
United Kingdom	National Policy run by 1999 Prime Ministers Initiative, implemented by the British Council	**C$ 900 million,** overall budget to the British Council, which has 250 offices in 110 countries, and 7000 employees. 1/3 of comes directly from the Government. The PMI added a further **C$ 13 million over 3 years specifically targeted at international education**.	Highly Skilled Migrants programme,	Similar to NZ
United States	No overarching national student recruitment policy. Provides extensive support through long established initiatives like the Fulbright scholarships, and through the State Department.	**Annual budget of C$ 380 million though** the State Department bureau of Educational and Cultural Exchange programs. (almost half goes to the Fulbright program). Education marketing services in every US Embassy abroad	Government policy does not lead in this area. Decreasing percentage of the international student market.	Applications accepted from those graduating from US institution, but only on the basis that they already have a H-1B work Visa. Employers have to petition for a change of status (usually a green card).

167

Canada		C\$ 1.6 million in the 2002 year total, In kind support for 17 Canadian Education Centres run by the CEC Network overseas, to cease in 2005	Nothing specifically as targeted as competitors strategies	Study in Canada and Canadian job experience recognized with additional points in immigration assessment. Proposed changes not included in recent legislation.

My office did a thorough analysis of the Canadian situation. We looked at the survey done by the office of CEC and compared this with our own experience at SLC.

St. Lawrence College

A passion for lifelong learning...

Strategies to Attract Top International Students and Faculty

A Synopsis

Canada's Innovation Strategy refers to the prospect of attracting top international students to help strengthen Canada's innovation capacity and enhance economic performance.**

Canada's major OECD competitors already have national polices in place to encourage, facilitate and welcome international students, as well as national objectives referring to related issues.**

Australia, New Zealand, the UK, Germany and France have specifically created, or increased financial support for, national bodies to market and promote their countries as "educational destinations" for international students.**

Many of Canada's OECD competitors have adapted their immigration policies to make it relatively easy for international students to remain in the host country permanently.**

Canada is unique within the OECD in that there is no national ministry of education, which would be the natural locus for the creation of an international education and recruitment policy. A lead federal government department should be identified to pursue such national objectives.**

Canadian immigration regulations should be amended to facilitate applications from top international students to remain in Canada.**

Increased financial support should be provided to both colleges and universities to attract top international students and to help keep Canadian researchers and scholars from leaving for greener pastures in the U.S.A. and elsewhere.**

Canada's dependence on U.S. markets (83 percent of our exports) is, in part, an indirect result of the lack of global exchange/recruiting of international students, scholars, workers and managers. The links that are built by students or workers who have lived, studied or worked in our country and our students and workers who have lived, studied or worked overseas are the foundation of a diversified international trade and business. Currently, Canada taps into only a fraction of the global market; our best ties, outside of the U.S. markets, are with Asian nations. This leaves an enormous pool of people and countries that are, so far, ignored.

Canada's first-class image is capital that we must build upon. This facet is completely underutilized; from the end of WWII until recently, immigration flowed well, without any effort. It was directed by a Department of Immigration and Manpower that knew the detailed needs of the labour market and therefore was in a position to adjust immigration accordingly. Now, we must invest

** Excerpted from CEC Network document: Strategies to Attract Top International Students and Faculty, A Comparative Study of Select OECD countries.

in this natural movement of people by offering incentives that make Canada even more attractive.

The logical first step is to create a welcoming and financially appealing atmosphere for international students who come here and for our students who go abroad; for example, offering exchange programs with free tuition. This is all directly linked to a national education policy.

Without a minimum of 200,000 immigrants a year, we are presently encountering a decline in the Canadian population. The First Nations are the only segment of our population that is experiencing some growth. Paul Martin's focus on native issues and native opportunities is therefore appropriate and long overdue.

Considering the above need to secure our nation's existence through immigration, it is difficult to understand why we are making immigration so restrictive. It is really a very bad policy to refuse the applications of international students based on the argument that they might use their studies as a means of staying in Canada once they have graduated. I cannot think of any better immigrants than people who have invested their money and energy into their studies at Canadian universities and community colleges. They have acquired a sound level of understanding of Canadian life and are willing to stay, to immigrate and to apply their youthful energy to our society.

Because of a lack of well-organized international student exchanges, our youth is not getting the benefit of the social, cultural and economical richness of such an experience. Less than 1 percent of our students go abroad and less than 1/2 percent of our total secondary and post-secondary students are international students. This is an indication of missed knowledge and missed opportunities.

The leading countries in the world outside North America are showing us the way with a student exchange of up to 5 percent. At the same time, when we look at their interdependence with their neighbours we notice that close allies and top trading partners do less than 10 percent of their trade among each other (for example, between the neighbours France and Germany). With 83 percent of our export going to the U.S.A., we have a long way to go, but we have without any doubt the same opportunities to improve this as any other country.

I remember clearly as a child, when Denmark was still mainly based on agriculture, a similar proportional percentage of the Danish exports went to the UK and Germany. Today, having evolved as a highly diversified industrial and agricultural society, Denmark does no more than 10 percent of the business with any one trading partner.

Development of a Federal/Provincial Policy and Standard on Education and Skills Training—Creating an Effective Policy on International Recruitment of Students and Scholars, as well as an Effective Exchange Program for Canadian Students

Working in a leadership role in the college system in Ontario, I can see how badly we are doing in funding post-secondary education. The more than 160,000 college students in Ontario are funded at a level that is approximately 40 percent below the Canadian national average, and the 300,000 university students are funded 18 percent below the Canadian national average. Both systems are funded at this low level in only one other jurisdiction in all of North America, and that is in the State of Alabama.

Why is the Canadian economy comparing so badly in one of the most important areas of training and post-secondary education? Even if Ontario is gaining by getting roughly 50 percent of all new immigrants to Canada, most of whom are highly skilled and trained, this is not sufficient on a long-term basis to compete in a national or international marketplace.

It is unbelievable that Ontario is limping behind most other provinces when it comes to funding of basic services, including training, post-secondary education, health services and funding of municipalities. Only less than 1 percent of all Canadian students tend to study outside their own province or country.

Canada has an estimated 58,000 international students who stay less than six months. These students, without a student visa, can enrol in any program without any restrictions other than the time limit. Furthermore, there are slightly less than 62,000 students on student visa as per the following tables:

Foreign Student Flows by Level of Study

Table 7
Foreign Student Flows by Level of Study

LEVEL OF STUDY	2002					2003					Difference
	Q1	Q2	Q3	Q4	Total	Q1	Q2	Q3	Q4	Total	2003 / 2002
Secondary or less	3,636	1,889	8,166	1,675	15,366	2,887	1,516	8,146	1,682	14,231	-7%
Trade	3,687	2,256	2,962	1,467	10,372	2,831	2,087	2,927	1,478	9,323	-10%
University	3,958	2,597	15,726	2,146	24,427	2,907	2,368	14,716	2,069	22,060	-10%
Other post-secondary	2,831	2,632	4,259	2,049	11,771	1,957	1,803	5,511	1,466	10,737	-9%
Other	2,016	2,187	1,865	816	6,884	1,249	1,348	1,594	761	4,952	-28%
Total	**16,128**	**11,561**	**32,978**	**8,153**	**68,820**	**11,831**	**9,122**	**32,894**	**7,456**	**61,303**	**-11%**

Table 8
Foreign Student Flows by Top Ten Source Countries

COUNTRY OF LAST PERMANENT RESIDENCE	2002						2003				
	Q1	Q2	Q3	Q4	Total	Rank	Q1	Q2	Q3	Q4	Total
South Korea	4,688	2,728	4,455	1,903	13,774	1	3,769	2,609	4,577	2,028	12,983
China	3,084	2,024	4,277	2,010	11,395	2	2,393	1,922	4,329	1,176	9,820
Japan	1,367	2,158	1,794	452	5,771	3	1,189	1,756	1,754	448	5,147
United States	596	395	2,743	321	4,055	4	299	285	2,844	312	3,740
France	556	173	2,610	182	3,521	6	254	131	2,812	199	3,396
India	224	218	1,279	313	2,034	8	232	273	1,443	361	2,309
Mexico	963	644	1,883	141	3,631	5	274	159	1,569	124	2,126
Germany	219	121	1,454	47	1,841	9	73	35	1,439	58	1,605
Taiwan	348	429	1,066	258	2,101	7	298	295	733	195	1,521
Hong Kong	206	107	918	174	1,405	10	197	59	821	167	1,244
Total — Top Ten Only		8,997	22,479	5,801			8,978	7,524	22,321	5,068	
Total — Other Countries	3,877	2,564	10,499	2,352	19,292		2,853	1,598	10,573	2,388	17,412
Total	**16,128**	**11,561**	**32,978**	**8,153**	**68,820**		**11,831**	**9,122**	**32,894**	**7,456**	**61,303**

Table 9
Foreign Student Flows by Destination

PROVINCE	2002					2003				
CENSUS METROPOLITAN AREA	Q1	Q2	Q3	Q4	Total	Q1	Q2	Q3	Q4*	Total
St. Johns	0	0	4	0	4	0	0	4	0	4
Other Newfoundland	58	51	181	28	318	47	23	197	30	297
Total Newfoundland	58	51	185	28	322	47	23	201	30	301
Total Prince Edward Island	**15**	**13**	**72**	**13**	**113**	**15**	**6**	**85**	**8**	**114**
Halifax	266	209	760	166	1,401	216	212	824	149	1,401
Other Nova Scotia	115	51	425	37	628	39	32	455	24	550
Total Nova Scotia	**381**	**260**	**1,185**	**203**	**2,029**	**255**	**244**	**1,279**	**173**	**1,951**
Saint John	51	31	145	29	256	17	34	108	28	187
Other New Brunswick	166	102	492	80	840	79	43	503	62	687
Total New Brunswick	**217**	**133**	**637**	**109**	**1,096**	**96**	**77**	**611**	**90**	**874**
Qubec	228	44	595	69	936	141	39	555	66	801
Montral	1,451	689	5,097	808	8,045	1,010	516	5,188	814	7,528
Ottawa — Gatineau (QC)	30	24	58	6	118	18	8	79	11	116
Other Quebec	215	107	749	151	1,222	130	75	861	117	1,183
Total Quebec	**1,924**	**864**	**6,499**	**1,034**	**10,321**	**1,299**	**638**	**6,683**	**1,008**	**9,628**
Ottawa — Gatineau (ON)	366	317	1,152	269	2,104	340	257	1,042	214	1,853
Toronto	3,472	2,734	5,535	2,029	13,770	2,745	1,996	5,574	1,691	12,006
Hamilton	466	167	618	176	1,427	366	150	651	133	1,300
London	145	74	532	86	837	106	87	479	79	751
Other Ontario	883	692	3,361	459	5,395	749	451	3,125	392	4,717
Total Ontario	**5,332**	**3,984**	**11,198**	**3,019**	**23,533**	**4,306**	**2,941**	**10,871**	**2,509**	**20,627**
Winnipeg	341	207	756	152	1,456	229	235	670	148	1,282
Other Manitoba	78	34	214	29	355	36	25	244	50	355
Total Manitoba	**419**	**241**	**970**	**181**	**1,811**	**265**	**260**	**914**	**198**	**1,637**
Regina	114	131	184	41	470	99	125	205	71	500
Saskatoon	80	62	215	53	410	71	38	261	53	423
Other Saskatchewan	33	23	174	11	241	32	17	208	22	279

173

Total Saskatchewan	227	216	573	105	1,121	202	180	674	146	1,202
Calgary	605	470	1,012	239	2,326	424	337	1,070	255	2,086
Edmonton	389	237	886	205	1,717	287	251	844	172	1,554
Other Alberta	214	166	550	70	1,000	168	126	537	76	907
Total Alberta	**1,208**	**873**	**2,448**	**514**	**5,043**	**879**	**714**	**2,451**	**503**	**4,547**
Vancouver	4,846	3,616	6,258	2,104	16,824	3,213	2,929	6,225	2,092	14,459
Victoria	136	130	409	49	724	101	120	336	65	622
Other British Columbia	1,338	1,165	2,492	782	5,777	1,134	978	2,509	616	5,237
Total British Columbia	**6,320**	**4,911**	**9,159**	**2,935**	**23,325**	**4,448**	**4,027**	**9,070**	**2,773**	**20,318**
Total Yukon	n/a	n/a	n/a	n/a	30	n/a	n/a	n/a	n/a	15
Total Northwest Territories	n/a	n/a	n/a	n/a	12	n/a	n/a	n/a	n/a	24
Total Nunavut	3	0	0	0	3	0	0	0	0	0
Not stated	20	13	22	6	61	13	7	28	2	50
Total	**16,128**	**11,561**	**32,978**	**8,153**	**68,820**	**11,831**	**9,122**	**32,894**	**7,456**	**61,303**

Citizenship & Immigration Canada

http://www.cic.gc.ca/english/monitor/issue05/04-students.html#table8

Of Canada's approx. 900,000 university students, 400,000 college students and 2,000,000 high school students, only a total of around 40,000 study outside the country.

The lack of a national policy on education and a strategy on student exchanges with certain standards, transfer guidelines and encouragement makes it very difficult to transfer students within Canada, or even within provinces, and almost impossible to create a satisfying exchange on an international level. This kind of a system has resulted in getting international students from mainly underdeveloped or emerging countries where the wealthy section of the population likes to send their students abroad and is prepared to pay our relatively high tuition and student fees. Most industrial developed countries have student exchange systems that allow students to move around from country to country without any major barriers. Tuition is either free or roughly the same in the host countries, which encourages students to go to other countries, experience a different culture/language, go through an exciting learning experience and encounter networking, exchanges and relationships that will enrich their lives and their opportunities in a wonderful way. This is the case within most European countries.

What Would a National Policy on Education and Training Look Like?

In my many discussions with politicians, the public service and business sector, I hear of many possible solutions and pathways out of the jungle of rules, local standards and stumbling blocks. There is no lack of solutions or feasible ways, but there is presently still a lack of willingness to make long overdue changes.

I live on one of the beautiful Thousand Islands between Kingston and Brockville, Ontario. In Kingston there is a large contingency of people who are either a part of the military, corrections, ministries or education. These people all have in common that their jobs move them around across Canada and beyond. They will all confirm how challenging it is for their children and spouses to adjust to new school systems, different legislation and worst of all very different curriculum and standards within Canada. This has nothing to do with cultural or intellectual diversity. It has more to do with waste of resources and talent and disrespect for more necessary standards.

Under a national policy on education, there is ample opportunity for provinces to develop their own direction, profile and outcome. The national policy would have one overarching goal: to ensure that standards within the country are compatible, transferable and up to speed by international comparison. Imagine the chaos if air transportation and safety standards were left to be governed by regional bodies. Today's world is increasingly global. If you want to produce a computer, a mobile phone or a car, the market expects a certain standard, quality and application. Today's world of communication makes everything accessible and transparent, and we better prepare ourselves to compete and succeed on this level.

The creation of a national policy on education (including post-secondary) and training will need its own home/ministry. The mandate of this ministry would be to support the provincial ministries without undermining the province' sovereignty. The goal would be to create certain standards for the curriculum and pathways for transfers, including approval of foreign credentials and exchanges of any kind. Again, this ministry could play a significant role in innovation within curriculum, research and development, and the skills agenda.

Summary

Are we as a nation willing and ready to engage in change? Darwin's quote is still with us:

"It's not the strongest of the species who survive, nor the most intelligent, but the ones most responsive to change."

Will our political leaders have enough foresight, courage and wisdom to lead Canada into a future that shows that we as a nation are the most responsive to change?

Being a leader in a community college, I am constantly challenged to change. It is clear that the global economy we are a part of is going through one of the fastest periods of change in mankind's history. If Canada wants to be a vibrant and leading part of the global community, we must embrace change and we must understand our challenges as opportunities. My introduction to change is meant as a joint brainstorming exercise and as an inspiration to move forward without a pre-fixed mind!

Let us jump on the train **"Enroute to Prosperity"** through education, healthy living and renewable energy as a symbol for our new direction.

Let us embrace the opportunities, and Canada's future will be bright!

Section Two

Food
For
Thought

An inspiration to eat and live smart.

Pollution of the environment, the waste of energy, unnatural nutrition, civilization diseases and drug addictions are problems of our time. Here to you are shown a few possible solutions.

The last part is a basic introduction to an optimal nutritional lifestyle designed to help you improve and maintain health. At the very end of part two I share information and numerous personal recipes to get you going.

Have fun!

Originally published in German, Danish and Russian in 1988 as *Perestroika, Our Environment and Food for the World*. Revised and updated English edition: Kingston, ON, Canada, Dec. 2003.

A Preamble and Foreword by the Author

This subject should not only concern Mr. Martin but also Mr. Bush, Mr. Blair, Mr. Schroeder, provincial leaders and every other world leader. In fact, it should concern every human being who feels a responsibility for, or who has an interest in, the survival of the human race and the planet we live on.

This is not meant to be a scientific paper; nor is it meant to be a political manifesto; but overall it is meant to deal with serious problems that affect our daily lives on this planet today. I have sorted out and analyzed all essential problems and worked out simple and practical solutions to each one. It is meant as an inspiration for all of us to think outside the box and to find solutions that will enable us to move forward in a positive way.

For many years I worked in the field of production and distribution of food. During this time I often travelled to other countries, and I realized that we are all suffering from the same technical evolution that was once celebrated as a blessing to mankind. The progress in technical and chemical industries has created many wonders, but there are boundaries that we have crossed over again and again without showing any inhibitions, and the consequences of our actions are catching up with us now.

There are fundamental problems in sectors of the farming industry, in the processing of natural and synthetic foods, and in all forms of environmental pollution and their subsequent aftermath. Additionally, drug addictions, other addictions and their associated problems will be addressed.

As we delve into these problems we can clearly see that there is a common thread, an underlying theme that exists through all contemplations and analyses: When the human race disregards the laws of nature because it believes it can make them its slave, it destroys or contaminates yet another part of our planet.

There is no exception to this rule.

All experiments that offend the rules of nature (i.e., increasing harvest with synthetic fertilizers and insecticides, mass production and slaughter of cattle, production of synthetic foods and the garbage associated with such food production and distribution) lead to the progressive destruction of our water resources, our environment, the atmosphere and our own bodies.

It is appalling to realize that our "throw-away society," according to EU statistics, produces 1000 kg of garbage per person per year in Europe. That amounts to 500,000,000,000 kg, or more than 50 million truckloads of waste. In North America, the amount is almost double; nearly 90 million truckloads of waste have to be processed every year, at the cost of more than $ 90 billion. Even greater is the waste of raw materials, such as crude oil or gas, resulting in catastrophic effects on the atmosphere, such as changes in the ozone layer and the "glasshouse effect."

It is disheartening to see new "civilization diseases" developing that are preventable, as they are largely due to processed foods, pollution of the environment, physiological pressures of our society and lack of physical exercise. Our health care and social services are becoming more complicated and expensive to maintain. We use about 10 percent of our gross national product to treat western degenerative diseases, and the resulting loss in hours worked costs the world, per annum, hundreds of billions of dollars. We know today that most forms of cancer and diseases of blood circulation are connected with our nourishment and the environment and our lack of physical exercise. Research in these areas has hardly brought us one step further. There are also no medications or sensational discoveries that can really help.

It is alarming in the face of an ever-increasing shortage of clean drinking water to know that 50 percent of the entire water consumption of the U.S.A. is for the irrigation of land for animal breeding and animal fodder. In America, this means a water consumption per meat eater of about 15,000 litres a day. For a lacto-ovo-vegetarian (with milk and egg production) the consumption is 5,000 litres, and for a pure vegetarian, only 1,000 litres per day.

If North American and European people would just give up 10 percent of their meat consumption, there would be no more hunger in the world. If they were prepared to reduce this by 20 percent, we could immediately prevent destruction of the tropical rain forests and much other old cultivation. If they were prepared to reduce meat consumption by 50 percent (i.e., an actual consumption of 50 kg per head per annum, which is still twice as high as the world average), then we could reduce meat production by 40 billion kilograms of meat in one year. This would mean that three to four billion additional people (allowing for population growth) could be fed, or more than half the world population could be nourished for free.

This is not something that I am proposing. I am just pointing out the enormous reserves that exist. All the talent and technical know-how that is presently available to mankind, combined with a little respect for flora and fauna and the human race, could create a good foundation for us to provide 6 to 10 billion people with enough first-class nutrition and space to live and breath in.

We are all jointly responsible for the past and even more so for taking steps for the future that will repair past mistakes and optimize future opportunities. Only if every single person takes responsibility for the environment and pays attention to the consequences of our actions can we master this task. We do not need to go back to the Stone Age, but we must develop technical methods in which the balance of nature is preserved and universal natural laws are obeyed.

The fundamental laws of nature are simple and clear. When we are prepared to accept the natural flow of things, then we can find a common way out of the present chaos into a peaceful, yet technically progressive world. The necessary reform to restore the balance of nature is, without doubt, the greatest challenge or opportunity for mankind since history began. All areas—military and civilian, agriculture and forestry, food production, automobile industry, shipbuilding, aeronautics, railway, chemical industry, packaging industry, commerce, banking, insurance, catering, energy supply, etc.,—are directly concerned and linked with this doubtlessly greatest and peaceful reform. No one can exclude himself with the usual apologies and the comment that one alone can accomplish nothing.

To be able to carry out these necessary curtailments, changes and improvements, new ways must be found for international co-operation. To succeed without getting lost in bureaucracy, we will need a new focus on the United Nations. They would need to be equipped with the necessary powers to be successful in blessing all mankind.

I beg all politicians, scientists and all my colleagues from education, industry and trade to honour this book as stimulation for new ideas to bring new developments for a better life.

Volker Thomsen, Kingston. September, 2004.

Chapter Twelve

Life Is Only Worth Living In Healthy Surroundings

It is obvious that overpopulation and every kind of pollution are leading us into a dead-end street. On one hand are the pessimists who say that it is not possible to save our planet. The ozone layer is getting thinner; large areas of tropical rain forests are being devastated; and the water reserves are more or less polluted. On the other hand are the optimists and the unsuspecting. They say we have had it all before and nothing happened, so we can carry on as we always have. However, anyone who has a bit of common sense can see that we are losing whatever control we had over the environment and our technology. It is just like the magician who conjured up a bad spirit and could not get rid of it again.

What possibilities remain for us, other than to find a prompt, international solution to all these problems? Tremendous political and economical solutions are necessary, but they are only feasible if they are supported and enforced by most countries and with consequence, credibility and commitment!

Therefore, the only solutions we can select are those that are convincing, not too complicated and able to be divided into practical steps, which then can be dealt with one at the time. This includes solving the immense economic problems of the former socialist countries and the Third World.

I believe there are a number of measures that can be effected, because they are simple, elementary, and seize all the roots of evil at once.

The only way back to a healthy environment must be a partial step back to the original form. No matter where we stand, we must be honest with ourselves and admit that in spite of our past achievements, we have made grave mistakes that we urgently need to correct. When I look back at my own past development in the food industry, I must admit that I had unknowingly been going in a false direction—all in the name of progress. I was convinced of the top quality of my products until indications showed that our industrialized and refined foods were creating problems of an unknown magnitude.

For someone who is very successful in the food processing industry, it is very inconvenient all of a sudden to know that extracted white flours and sugar are a threat to our health. All production facilities, recipes and even the markets are based on these products. When you have friends, contacts and partners in the business, it is difficult to make them understand that you no longer can work in the industry without changing it. It is even more difficult to explain to them that you may have to leave the industry and them if they are not able or willing to go along.

Once it was clear to me that I was working in an industry that, either intentionally or not, was causing suffering for future generations through incorrect nutrition, I immediately wanted to turn my back on my life's work. It is difficult though to leave one's friends and old surroundings. They are still your friends even if they are not willing to change. In this transition period, my friends would reason, "if we don't produce these products, other companies will, and how can we possible convert to new ways/products without losing the present business?"

Therefore, I reluctantly sold my shares and decided to work on solutions, finding sensible improvements by every means available.

Health Is the Most Important Basis for a Life that Is Worth Living

There are medical and political schools of thought that claim that the standard of health in the world has never been better than it is today. They refer to increased life expectancy statistics in the Western world but forget very conveniently that the mortality rates give no information as to the level of health of the present population. High infant mortality rates and deaths from infections and epidemics reduced the expectancy of life in the past and are still doing so today in some underdeveloped countries.

It is a fact—and herein lies the contradiction—that mankind is ill more frequently and by an abundance of new illnesses. In spite of advances being made in medical research, the situation is becoming increasingly unpredictable and the state of health of the civilized world is getting worse and worse.

In a country like Germany (the figures are comparable with those of U.S.A., Canada or the Common Market), the cost of the health services has already increased to over 3,000 Euros per head per annum, with a constantly rising tendency. This is more than 12 percent of the gross income, in spite of all attempts to economize services.

More and more people are experiencing complaints of the digestive system. Half the population has some form of constipation, and it is a vicious circle, which is intensified by regularly taking laxatives. This frequently results in artificial bowels.

Nearly 25 million people are suffering from rheumatism in Germany (1/3 of the population). In Canada the cause for this is often blamed on the northern climate, although similar numbers of people in the southern parts of the U.S.A. are suffering to the same degree as Canadians in the north. Over 30 percent of the masculine population dies from heart or circulatory diseases. Approximately 30 percent of the population dies from some sort of cancer. At the turn of the century, this was less than 3 percent.

187

Help—I'm Fat!

It sounds strange, but most fat people are undernourished.

Their obesity is due to one-sided diets, which usually consist of foods that are dead-energy carriers, such as sugar or extracted white flour. This can lead to a chronic lack of vital substances, which means that the person has a permanent urge for nutrients and therefore feels hungry. Eating the same inferior foods cannot satisfy the real need. Reducing diets also will not replace these vital substances. Repeatedly we see how people who have taken so many pains just to lose a few pounds quickly put them on again after a short time. Sometimes they will gain more than before the diet.

Most fat people are undernourished

There is only one thing that can help: whole food. Nature actually designed our foods in exactly the way we need them to be.

It is possible, with the knowledge that we have today, to correct many past mistakes. Why don't we do this?

What Are Dead Food Carriers?

Nature has composed our nutrition in a perfect way. Fruit, nuts, grains and vegetables are all created as whole(some) products that contain all the building blocks necessary to be digested without adding any substances other than our saliva and digestive juices.

For example, to digest grains or whole-grain products properly it is very important that we chew them thoroughly. Our saliva contains numerous inorganic salts and organic substances like enzymes and ptyalin, which in combination start the digestion process in our mouth while we are chewing. When we then swallow this mash, it is ready to go through digestion and absorption to be fully utilized.

By comparison, if we want to digest refined flour, a lot of the substances needed to break down the food are missing and not available. The missing natural vitamins in the white flour will still be needed for digestion, and because they are not contained in the mush they need to be extracted from our bodies.

Therefore all products like refined sugar and flour or products containing these are a real challenge to be digested properly without depriving our system of these vital substances. The result is that these refined and changed products used over a long period create major deficiencies and make us sick. Therefore they are rightfully called "dead calorie or food carriers."

Why Has the Medical Profession Failed?

We ask ourselves, why doesn't my doctor give me better advice? It is incomprehensible when a doctor gives a patient who is suffering from constipation a chemical laxative. With a diet of natural, whole foods, constipation could be successfully treated in most cases. In reality, with the right diet it usually eventually corrects itself. On the other hand, prescribing a chemical medication can be the start of a vicious circle for a patient, which ends in the destruction of the natural bowel flora. Similar examples can be given in respect to practically all Western civilization diseases. The patient receives a medicine from his doctor that immediately alleviates his complaint, but in most cases there is no immediate fix, and the foundation of a chronic illness is often laid because there was no real attempt to start a proper healing in the first place.

What does a cross-section of the patients in a waiting room look like? Most of their illnesses are in the range of colds, infectious diseases, digestive complaints, disturbances of the circulation, allergies and diseases caused by environmental pollution. When we make an accurate analysis, we come to the conclusion that nearly all these diseases have something to do with incorrect nourishment, lifestyle or the environment.

Inherited diseases or illnesses caused through accident must of course be omitted, although some inherited diseases have their roots in the poor nourishment of our forefathers.

The roots of our unhealthy eating habits can be found in industry, agriculture and, in part, also in the medical profession. Unfortunately, in the past medical schools did not put much emphasis on the importance of nutrition, lifestyle and exercise in relation to health. We know today that there are connections between correct nourishment and social health, which indicates a need to make this a primary focus in medicine today.

Our government needs to change and supplement the education system to reflect the new insights and knowledge that research is revealing. All doctors, nurses, teachers and helpers need to upgrade their training in nutrition, lifestyle and exercise to the same standards as a newly trained physician.

Why Hasn't the Public Been Told?

There are many experts, scientists and doctors who have found a connection between nutrition and good health. Why is this knowledge not extended to the public more widely by the press and by the authorities? One comes to the conclusion that only things that make a profit are worth knowing. It seems that these unbiased results from research are only acknowledged by a minority of idealists, who are usually labelled as being neurotic.

The fact that the public is told so little creates a gap that should be filled as soon as possible. In actual fact, the difficulties are easy to solve. It is possible, in a reasonable space of time, to carry out a very effective awareness campaign, as proposed in my paper "Canada Eat and Live Smart" (see pg. 51).

In school we learn many important and useful things. However there is an obvious lack of information, especially in primary schools, on the practical side of life, such as nutrition, sports, the environment and the community in which we live.

We can only experience respect and love for our food, our environment and our fellow citizens when we are raised to perceive and comprehend these values from childhood onward. When we recognize the connections between the natural flow of things and their conformity, we will be able to feel the necessary appreciation and respect for our unique environment.

Therefore, it is crucial that these subjects are dealt with intensively in our schools. The government should be inspired to make comprehensive changes to the curriculum, which should include all aspects of proper diet and lifestyle. There are many good Canadian and international examples of how effective an early introduction is. This is the fastest route to introducing health awareness and positive lifestyle change in the entire population. Good health throughout a lifetime is only possible when we eat natural, healthy foods and have enough physical exercise.

There are many differing opinions about healthy food and also many prejudices and misunderstandings. It is shocking to realize how little most of the "experts" know about healthy foods. Only a small number of physicians and a modest part of the pharmaceutical/chemical industry seem to know the important, basic rules for good nourishment. On the other hand, farmers or makers of processed foods seem better informed, possibly because just sixty years ago most food industries along with renowned scientists were still promoting refined sugars and flours as good nutritional value and highly recommended these as part of the daily diet. In the beginning of my career in food processing, I also was totally convinced that all our processed products with their long shelf lives were healthy and of top quality. The effect of processing and refining in most cases means creating a durable product, which is easy to store and prepare but has an inferior nutritional value and is a carrier of dead energy.

Today I am more than grateful to all the people who have explained these basic rules to me and helped me change my diet and

191

lifestyle. Changing my personal way of life has given me back 100 percent vitality, and I have lost sixty pounds. I was fascinated to learn by experience that, as long as you don't eat anything refined or processed, your body will get the needed nutrition and the weight disappears by itself. This change in my life had a significant impact on my career as a food producer.

The first basic rule: One should only eat pure, biological and natural foods.

The second basic rule: These foods should be heated as little as possible, and, preferably, no preserving agents should be added. This means that one should only eat products that are fresh or that have been heated up quickly.

The third basic rule: Our food should predominately consist of fresh whole food. Animal foods, including milk, milk products and eggs, should only play an underlying role, especially as the eating of meat is expensive and can even be unhealthy. If one cannot live without eating meat, then one must follow certain rules, as meat is not very digestible when combined with carbohydrates.

Eating any number of unhealthy, artificial and partially tasteless mass products created by modern industrial society, in combination with too little physical exercise, has led to degeneration of our bodies. This is a double burden.

This is substantiated by the state of health of a population in times of need. Numerous analyses have been made during and after the two world wars. They clearly show that when there is a shortage of animal products the health of the nation is superior when compared to times of abundant food supply. This can be supported by the fact that in time of shortage there is also a decreased supply of sugar and denatured extracted flour products.

The Consumption of Dead-Energy Carriers, Such as sugar, Extracted White Flour and Polished Rice, etc., Makes Us Ill

Scientific research supports the fact that the above-named products are responsible for many illnesses. The degeneration of tissues takes about fifteen to thirty years, and a complete renewal of these is most unlikely. The only possibility to stop the process of degeneration is to change to whole foods. The lifespan of a rat is approximately one or two years, each year equivalent to twenty-five human years. In experiments with rats, one group was fed with wheat grain and the other group with extracted white flour, over a period of one to two years. The first group remained healthy, but the second group was in a wretched condition and came to a miserable end. I could give details of many other experiments on animals, but they all prove more or less the same thing.

I made an astonishing discovery—there are connections between addictions and inferior nutrition.

Most physical illnesses can be connected with various factors, whereby the right sort of nourishment and physical exercise are just as important as hereditary factors and the physiological influence of the environment. It is, therefore, quite logical to assume that mental illnesses, addictions and depression have the same relationship to these factors. The internal restlessness, the inability to adjust and the tendency to addiction of the civilized human being show a direct connection to the unnatural way of life of modern industrial society and its unnatural way of eating.

A sick person would seek immediate relief for aches and pains. Our society makes it easy to receive this relief quickly. All we need to do is to go to the nearest doctor, who then prescribes us some sort of drug to get rid of the aches and pains as soon as possible. The result is that when the patient is free from pain we believe the treatment is completed, and subsequently a proper cure or healing is never undertaken. Drug addicts go through a similar process. They slip from one shot to the other, not realizing that they are slipping into an abyss from which, in nearly all cases, there is no return. If my theory is correct, then there is no hope for the treatment of drug addiction and all other illnesses, especially the diseases of modern civilization, without returning to a holistic method including natural foods. Therefore, I can only advise all general practitioners and all those it may concern to study the subject of whole foods and to adapt this way of good nourishment together with sufficient exercise, which definitely increases the chances of recovering overall good physical and mental health.

Chapter Thirteen

Nutrition a Hundred Years Ago and Nutrition Today

Only products that are pure can be seen as natural and valuable to our health. In this category are all types of full-grain cereals, nuts, fresh fruit and vegetables. From the category "animal foods" we can include fresh milk and eggs, and for our thirst, fresh spring water, small amounts of freshly pressed juices from fruit and vegetables (only small amounts, as these refreshments should be considered as part of our food intake and also because of an eventual overdose of certain fruits or vegetables) and various fruit and herbal teas.

The more we look back into the past, the more we see how naturally the foods were prepared. The industrial revolution brought the various preserving agents that were added to sugar and flour. A hundred years ago, the supply and demand of food was much simpler and one-sided, and still it was much healthier and digestible. Why? An important part of the food was made up of cereals in their natural form, and these were eaten as either porridge or bread. Unprocessed wholemeal cereals contain virtually all the necessary ingredients, including proteins. Everybody should eat two to three tablespoonfuls of wholemeal cereals or whole rice a day in order to obtain the vital ingredients that are needed for a healthy life. The best way is to eat tasty muesli for breakfast. I will be writing about the best ingredients for this muesli later on.

Today, the greatest part of our diet consists of dead food. Belonging to these dead foods are pastas, bread and cakes made from white flour, confections, chocolate, puddings, heated fruits and fruit juices made from concentrated fruits. Even the so-called reform foods from health food shops, such as ready-made muesli and oat flakes, etc., are by no means as healthy or of the highest quality as fresh-made whole-grain muesli or oat flakes. Many people today who to the best of their knowledge eat "healthy" foods still eat dead foods without knowing it.

A product such as sugar with all its harmful side effects is certainly not as dangerous to the health as alcohol, nicotine or addictive drugs, but nevertheless, over a long period the effects of a regular intake can be devastating. The same thing goes for extracted white flour and products containing it.

The Healthy Nourishment of Primitive Folk

A set of teeth is like a barometer. Through the changes in the formation of the teeth and gums, a dentist can see the appearance of degeneration that is a result of consuming unnatural, processed foods. It is not surprising that dentists have gained much more from the research in the fields of nutrition than other doctors.

Dr. Schnitzer, a German dentist, has been a pioneer in this field of research for decades. Although Dr. Schnitzer is a vegetarian and does not recommend the eating of meat, his book, *Schnitzer Intensive Foods and Whole-Foods* (Schnitzer Publishing, St. Georgian, Germany), is the perfect introduction into a whole-food diet. He gives a very detailed summary of important facts about whole foods. In Canada you can find books from other authors covering the same subject. This chapter gives you an excellent introduction into his recommendations, which partly are included in my own recipes, even if they are modified to my personal taste. When you venture out into the more wholesome direction, you should still follow your taste and your own desires rather than other people's direction. As long as you stick to the basic rules, you will be fine.

It is absolutely necessary that everyone who changes to a whole-food diet should look at all the facts, especially when changing to a complete vegetarian diet. It must be said that a whole-food diet can be with or without meat. Our eating traditions are more or less built upon nourishment that includes meat, from which we obtain a part of our vitamins, minerals and proteins. Any change should therefore be made very carefully to ensure that we do not suffer from any deficiencies.

During the first half of the last century, Dr. Price, an American dentist, studied the eating habits of the last remaining primitive people on earth. He came to some very astounding results, and these are described very convincingly and in great detail in the book *The Human Race in Jeopardy*, published by Hippocrates Books. Dr. Price primarily studied the teeth of these primitive people. He examined them in their natural environment and again when they had come into contact with civilization and processed foods. He came across the same phenomenon again and again.

As long as these people lived in their natural surroundings and ate their customary foods, they remained healthy and were seldom susceptible to any weaknesses or diseases. Their teeth remained healthy for life, and they did not suffer from the usual symptoms of old age. Once they came into contact with civilization and started eating processed foods, they eventually started to suffer from all the modern diseases we know. These include caries (decay of a bone or tooth), a general deterioration of bodily resistance and immune system, complaints of the digestive system, rheumatism, and cancer, etc.

Children in the first generation of processed foods are already suffering from caries, often from a narrowing of the upper middle jaw, changes in the shape of the nose that causes difficulties in breathing, sometimes even a negative change in character. An example for this is the sudden tendency to depression. These types of ailments and mental illnesses together with aggression are seldom seen in primitive folk.

Price located all the known groups of people who were enjoying nourishment from pure, biological foods. These groups at the beginning of the last century were: the Natives of the Swiss mountain valleys; the natives on the Hebrides; the Indians in South and North America; some traditional Eskimos in North America and Greenland; the farming and hunting natives of Africa, the aborigines in Central and Coastal Australia, in Polynesia, Malaya; and the natives of North India. They had one thing in common. They all benefited from pure whole-food nutrition. They retained their health and resistance over hundreds of years and, although they have lived in small isolated groups, there was no sign of incest.

During his investigations, Price could not make any real differentiation between diets consisting of meat, fish, vegetarian or mixed diets, although he did discover that the people living in North India, who are vegetarians, were the healthiest. Essential for healthy nourishment is that the food is completely, purely, biological whole-food nourishment. He discovered that Eskimos, although their main diet consists of meat and fish, get enough vitamins and minerals from animal intestines supplemented with berries and seaweed to make up a natural whole-food diet. However, it must be said that the life expectancy of meat-eating Eskimos is not as high as that of the mixed diet or vegetarian nourished natives of other countries.

If Dr. Price could see how much more the health of most of these groups has deteriorated due to their continued change in lifestyle, he would be shocked to see that his findings were probably understated. Up to 40 percent of First Nations people in Canada developed type 2 diabetes in the last few generations, which shows us that they are more sensitive to the effects of the denatured products and the lack of exercise.

The findings of Dr. Schnitzer and Mr. Price made me take special notice of the traditional way of cooking in various regions when travelling. During prolonged stays in my wife's hometown, Hangzhou, in the province of Zhejiang in China, I reached an astounding conclusion. Although Hangzhou belongs to one of the oldest cultivated and yet civilized cities of the world, because of its climate and geography it still offers an abundance of natural, whole foods. Unfortunately, a large range of processed foods such as polished white rice, white flour, sugar and processed oil are also consumed. Still, the greatest part of the nourishment consists of pure whole foods that are only heated up for a very short period at high temperatures. Therefore the nourishment here is, without doubt, more abundant in vitamins and minerals than is usual in other parts of the civilized world.

The result of this can clearly be seen when you compare people's appearance, teeth and skin from the various areas in China. People coming from places where the diet is closer to a Western diet show greater levels of degeneration.

Dr. Price discovered that the primitive nutrition of the natives that were examined had one thing in common. Their nutrition had a greater quota of minerals and vitamins than that of the industrial civilization—as a rule, four to ten times as much. I can confirm this through my own observations in Hangzhou and elsewhere.

By chance I made an astounding discovery. Gradually, over a number of years, I had reduced my meat intake, feeling inclined to become a vegetarian. It was therefore with some aversion that I saw my wife eating a small tortoise. This was served to her after my mother-in-law heard that she was pregnant. Like all other dishes in China, the tortoise had only been heated at a high temperature for a short time. My wife ate it with great relish and, as is the custom in China, only the shell remained! I noticed the same thing at all other private and official invitations. The whole of the animal is consumed. From poultry only the feathers remain; even the bones are chewed and sucked out. After eating fish, the only remains are the larger bones. It is the same procedure with other meats; for instance, with crustaceans such as crabs or shrimps, only the hardest shell pieces are spat out.

Here lies a further important key to the right nutrition. We come to the conclusion that all whole-food diets, whether vegetarian or with meat, are only whole-food diets when all parts of the original products are eaten. This means eating the whole-grain, the entire fruit including some of the peel, the entire vegetable and, last but not least, meat and fish with all digestible parts, including the crackling, the sinews, the gristle, the bone marrow, the insides and the brains. However, I do need to remark that, even if these rules are valid, we have to be very cautious in our consumption, particularly of animal fats or denatured vegetable oils. We are not getting enough physical exercise to tolerate a high fat intake. In a recent study conducted with Mennonites, it was proven that their fairly high fat content diet has no negative impact because of their traditional behaviour. For instance, they walk or move around ten times as much as the rest of us and burn off the fat, as long as these are not trans fatty acids, which would cause problems even for them.

The preparation of the food is as important as the wholeness. We should avoid cooking, grilling or frying foods for long periods, as this partially or completely destroys all vitamins and proteins. However the average American-way of cooking is far removed from these natural foundations. It is important and essential for the health of the people of America that they retreat from taking the leading role in the processed food industry and find their way back to more natural foods.

How Nourishing Should Be and Is It Tasty?

I have briefly dealt with the basic rules for a reasonable and healthy diet, but how can we incorporate this in real life? Many people imagine that changing over to whole foods means going without this or that. We are all creatures of habit, but with the right kind of motivation and a little knowledge it is not difficult to give them up and change to enjoy wholesome foods. Everybody should know that changing over to a whole-food diet will not mean restrictions. On the contrary, you may be surprised how versatile it can be, perhaps even more so than today's average way of eating. In addition, more consciousness of what we are eating increases the quality of our food automatically. The result of a well-balanced vitamin-rich diet and a change in eating techniques will increase the delights of eating enormously. All of this without regret, because we do not put on any weight. By eating whole foods our bodies find their own ideal weight and stay there.

The challenge will be to understand undernourishment and its effects that have evolved over a long period of time. It will therefore take some time and patience before our system will be in balance again. We need to understand that, just as in medicine, there is no quick fix available in nutrition either. This is one reason why most diets only work for a short time, because usually after a short period we take up our beloved habits again and the vicious circle starts all over.

To try and prevent prejudices arising through the assumption that whole food is more expensive than normal food, I have studied this in detail, and here are my conclusions. Meat, fish and cheese are more expensive than other foods; whole food is more expensive than processed foods; but in the long run whole food is still cheaper than a normal mixed diet with meat, cheese and processed foods. In my own family of four we can save about 20 percent per month. Fortunately, organic cultivation is becoming more and more popular, and therefore these products can be sold more reasonably. You also must consider that a small organically grown apple usually contains more vitamins than a big, shiny, industrially grown apple. Once your body has arrived at its own balance, there will be reduced consumption because of the better nutrients in whole organic foods.

Everyone who wishes to change to whole foods should make a comprehensive study of all literature on this subject. My book gives only an overall view of whole foods and at the same time explains the economic and political ties. There are many good books, as well as cookbooks, on whole foods. I read all the relevant books I could find, From Dr. Schnitzer's *Intensive Foods/Normal Foods* to *Fit for Life* by an American couple, Mr. and Mrs. Diamond. After reading these various books I adopted the most convincing theories, to which I have added my own discoveries. *Our Food Our Destiny* by Dr. M.O. Bruker, (Emu Books, 5420 Lahnstein, West Germany, presently only available in German) I found the most helpful. In his book, Dr. Bruker describes in a clear and understandable way all the things we need to know about our food. In relationship to meat consumption, the same can be said for the book *Diet of a New America*, written by John Robbins (Stillpoint Publishing, Walpole, NH, U.S.A.). This disturbing book gives detailed information on the cruel and true facts of how mass breeding, holding and slaughtering of animals is carried out and as a result how inferior most of the products are. Another book that will be particularly appealing to people older than forty is *Longevity* by W. Lee Cowden, M.D., Ferre Akbarpour, M.D., Russ Dicarlo and Burton (Alternative Medicine Books, www.alternativemedicine.com). Because our physical fate is determined very early, I would recommend this book to everybody. It informs us about most of the important aspects of physical well-being.

Although I will be going into some detail about food and its preparation, in this book I would like to highlight the economic and political factors. The information that Dr. Bruker shared in his book *Unsere Nahrung unser Schicksal* ("Our Food Our Destiny") can be, in effect, transferred to politics and economics.

In the late eighties when the Soviet Union experienced a big undersupply of food and needed help from the world, Mr Gorbachev could have temporarily solved his political and economic problems. He only would have needed to throttle meat and liquor production by 20 percent and he would have had a surplus of food. We must not forget that when we convert grain or vegetables into animal fodder there is only a return of about 20 percent (milk) and something like 6 percent (meat/fat). Fifteen times as much grain is needed to feed the cattle for meat production than to use grain as a direct source of energy for humans. Poultry and pork are a little more efficient with rates of seven to ten times. If the Soviet Union had changed over to a pure vegetarian diet, it could have comfortably fed something like 1.2 billion people with the amount of food available. This compares with the situation in China today where there is only moderate (but unfortunately quickly growing) meat consumption. The change in China, with substantial increases in meat, milk and refined products consumption, will be the biggest challenge for that evolving nation. We need to understand these facts in order to relate them to our own situation.

For a satisfactory conversion to whole-food nutrition, one must understand and master the most important factors. However, that is not enough. It is just as important to have the right recipes at hand so that whole-food cooking can be a real treat. Every country has its own range of good raw and whole-food cookbooks. The best products can be supplied locally, and it is therefore important, when possible, to use cookbooks on local wholesome foods.

Our present methods of cooking with unnatural processed foods and most of our eating habits have been developing over generations. It is therefore necessary during our conversion to have patience with ourselves. So much more pleasing is the end result when the conversion has been successful in all points. One must take one step after another, and in this way one can experience many small successes without being under pressure. The recipes at the end of the book will also help you to get started and find your way. When we first germinate seeds in a germinating pot and we see good results, or when we bake our first wholemeal bread and the tasty smells float through the house, then we can eat with relish our own self-made products and quite rightly be proud of them.

As a result of combing through the facts you will gradually be in possession of so much knowledge that an automatic rise in the quality of your cooking will be the result. This means that you will identify yourself with the dishes you cook and you will develop your own "Cultivated Kitchen" of which you can be very proud. We are all individuals with our own needs and tastes. These can both be satisfied through whole-food cooking and by turning our backs on those unnatural processed foods that ultimately will make us sick.

Chapter Fourteen

The Farming Industry Today

Not only do we nourish ourselves in the wrong way by eating too many "dead" foods but we also take in many toxic substances. These come from the modern fertilizers, insecticides, fungicides and other forms of environmental pollution.

This is crowned by the present methods of cultivation and the degrading ways in which animals are bred. Mass animal breeding brings an almost unbeatable problem, getting rid of manure. We know how problematic it is getting rid of human excrement and sewage, especially in highly populated areas, but worse still, rivers and seas are still used for this purpose. In North America and Europe the current volume of animal manure and urine is twenty times higher than that of humans.

However the excess manure could and should be utilized as another resource. In many European countries and particularly in Scandinavia, alternative energies play a large role and biomass reactors are used widely in farm areas, for excess manure in combination with fat extracted from restaurants waste water and other organic wastes. In Canada we are very familiar with biomass, with a substantial capacity of almost 2000 MW. If this technology had been used more widely, and particularly for excess manure, the water contamination in Walkerton, Ontario, could easily have been prevented.

Just as devastating are the statistics over the loss of forests and woodlands. Since 1960, the tropical rain forests in Central America have decreased from 350,000 square kilometres to 200,000 square kilometres due to cultivation. In South America, even larger forest areas have been sacrificed for building roads and grazing cattle. It is the same situation in Africa, Asia and even in Europe and North America. Since 1965, more than 19.5 million acres of forest have been made arable for cattle breeding. At the same time, the world loses an area much bigger than Germany every year to erosion, which is caused by making the forest arable. Nature takes about 200 years to develop a good soil, about one centimetre every ten years. In the U.S.A., the loss every year is about 4.9 million acres or about 2,500,000,000 tons of soil or 11,000 kg per person. Former tropical rain forests converted to grazing land have become so barren that 2.5 acres provides grass for only one cow. After ten years of use, the remaining soil is usually so exploited and weakened that one cow will need ten times as much (twenty-five acres).

At the same time, our earth is being covered with mono cultures, and even greater quantities of predominately tasteless food is being processed from soil that is susceptible and sick. It is out of the question to speak about a balance of nature.

The development in the farm industry is similar. In the past, farms were well-balanced structures. The balance between the production of grain, vegetables and breeding of cattle was the same as between arable land, meadowland, fallow land, marshland and woodland. Most farms were independent units. They supplied themselves with cattle feed, fertilizers, and food and could even produce by-products such as clothes and simple tools and utensils. Processing and storage were usually accomplished with simple but efficient methods. With love, care and regular turning, the threshed grain could be kept alive and fit for storage for many years. Every grain, a miracle of nature, was in an edible state and contained nearly everything that was necessary for a person to live a healthy life. The same could be said for many other products that could be conserved in a natural way without being destroyed by modern processing techniques and preserving agents.

The farming industry should not be blamed for the changes that have taken place. On the contrary, because of worldwide competition, farmers are being forced into applying industrial methods of cultivation in order to survive. However, mass-cattle breeding, apart from the wrenched and undignified existence of these caged-up animals, leads to poor quality meat, and the volume of manure that has to be disposed of burdens the environment to such an extent that future fresh-water supplies are in danger.

Although the facts are well known to the chemical industry, the agricultural industry, the manufacturers and the politicians, no viable solutions or attempts to change have been made. Whole areas of the Third World are being devastated by mismanagement of developmental aid with its misguiding recommendations. Countries that were once able to produce and supply their own food are now dependent on supplies from food manufacturers of the industrial countries. Of course there are positive forms of developmental aid work, but they will remain the exception if the failures in the present international aid are not corrected. Internationally valid regulations and laws should be enforced through the framework of the United Nations organization for an improvement in the breeding of animals and the cultivation of agricultural products.

Harmful Substances in Our Food

Our present food is full of many foreign and harmful substances, including poisons. There is a very significant book from Eva Kapfelsperger and Udo Pollmer dtv Munich, with the significant title *Iss und Stirb* (*Eat and Die*). If we continue to systematically destroy our environment, we could reach the point where we cannot eat anything without being in actual danger. The dangerous substances from pesticides, fertilizers and fungicides in our food have reached such an alarming level that they should be internationally prohibited.

Apart from the above-named harmful substances in our food, there are many more, such as heavy metals and chemicals of all kinds, including mineral oils. Last but not least is the great number of chemicals and preserving agents that get into our food through processing.

Synthetic/Artificial Fertilizers and Pesticides

Our soil is made up of a natural composition of various substances. In one gram or one teaspoon (1/30 of one ounce) of earth we can find up to 18 million bacteria, one million fungi and over one million individual cells. Just as plants need these organisms to live and for nourishment, the organisms themselves need nourishment. Therefore it is as important for the plant as it is for us to be supplied with the nourishment of whole foods. When the balance of nature is destroyed, plants develop diseases just as we do, and this leads to an increase in the appearance of pests. The result is a new demand on pesticides, and there we are, back to the same old vicious circle.

The goal is to find a way back to a more natural and balanced agricultural system that needs no poisonous pesticides.

In view of the reasons given above, synthetic fertilizers and pesticides should be prohibited or limited. Exceptions should only be applied when the soil is lacking some nutrient or mineral. This should be based on an exact timetable, because the soil is so sick from decades of artificial cultivation and the use of pesticides. It is very important that all measures taken be coordinated. It is ineffective to limit or prohibit the use of pesticides if synthetic fertilizers and fungicides are not also prohibited. Only when the soil has recovered its natural fertilizers can the repair begin.

If we could come to an international agreement to reduce synthetic fertilizers and pesticides, then the yield in kilograms would automatically fall. At first this would mean a bottleneck situation but at the same time an overdue reduction in the production of inferior products. The nutrition value would be better, and the environment would improve. A limited use of synthetic fertilizers and pesticides and a reduction in meat production would automatically lessen the burden on the environment.

An international committee should publish a list of all natural fertilizers, the wise use of which would have a positive effect on the soil and as a result not demand a heavy use of pesticides. This sector of the agriculture industry should be newly organized, and this offers a chance for all types of organic waste to be brought into the planning.

Radiation

The ever-growing burden of radiation on the environment and our food, in the water and in the atmosphere, is becoming a threat to mankind. All the other so-called artificial environmental interferences that have damaged our health and changed the balance of nature are harmless in comparison to the damage that is being caused by radiation.

These damages are of lasting duration and can hardly be repaired. All ionic rays have the same effect on cells. The fermentation system becomes blocked; the water in the cells becomes ionized; the chromosomes start breaking up; and the ribonucleic acids that are connected to the amino acids are destroyed. These lead to serious illnesses and damage that sometimes appears years later, such as leukemia and cancer. Especially sensitive to all radiation rays are the gene cells. When a gene is damaged, the radiation rays cause a defect that affects many future generations.

Atomic weapons and atomic energy have brought a temporary world freedom and a relatively good source of energy. Contamination through radiation has, however, crippled complete regions. The mutations are irreparable, and further damage can only be prevented if all atomic weapons and atomic power stations are abolished and shut down.

In summary, we can see that all the manipulations that mankind has made in nature have not brought many positive results. Most so-called progress in this field has turned out to be something that has only destroyed the balance of nature.

1. Synthetic fertilizers and pesticides have given temporary good harvests but unfortunately of inferior quality and taste. The international competition in the agriculture industry for "better" and bigger harvests has opened the door for the chemical industry to produce more and more reckless products. The result: a healthy chemical industry and a soil that is sick.

2. Industrial processed "dead" foods, such as sugar, extracted white flour, and industrial fats and oils, have no doubt a few great advantages, as they can be stored longer, have good processing possibilities and look good. However, they make us ill and tired. Because of the resulting lack of vitamins and other important nutrition, mankind is, in spite of the oversupply of calories and the associated overweight, undernourished.

The Present Processing of Food

At the beginning of the industrialization of food processing, the desire was to produce food that was lasting and of good quality. Through tremendous technical progress in this field, the goal was reached—unfortunately, with bitter results. When food is processed and preserving agents are added, food is changed so unnaturally that it becomes a carrier of "dead" energy, and the change has caused mankind much damage in its development.

This knowledge is of course, relatively new. A few years ago, most of the food-scientists believed refined sugar to be a high quality food. It was the same with extracted white flour. Ballast stuffs were separated and, since they were then considered poor quality products, were used as animal fodder. People suffering from stomach/digestive ailments were put on especially fine diets consisting of boiled and processed products, such as rusk (extracted white flour and sugar), black tea, potato puree and fine milk soups. What these patients really needed, however, in their weak condition was a diet of fresh whole foods.

Another example is the processing of milk. When the so-called UH Milk (ultra heated) was developed, it was seen as *the* sensation because it can be kept so long. Today we know that this milk can only be considered a low-quality partial food due to the fact that it has gone through so many processing procedures. In spite of this, it continues to be very popular and nobody thinks of informing the consumer of its inferior quality. Pasteurized whole milk is not much superior. The vitamin and protein content has also partly been destroyed through heating, and the milk on the market can only be considered as an inferior-quality partial food. Only the milk directly from the cow, not processed in any way, can be called whole food.

In 1962 I started my first factory for the mass production of food and was full of enthusiasm at the possibilities of extensions and improvements in this industry. I was a small but successful manufacturer and distributor and visited many other large and smaller factories, which all had the same target: rationization and conserving food products to the blessing of mankind. I was as impressed as the others at the ever-increasing yield of the harvests per acre. And I was inspired by one thought alone, to develop even better and more durable packages and products. If at that time anyone had told me about unnatural foods, I would no doubt have shrugged my shoulders and shaken my head over such strange thoughts.

Although there was some knowledge about whole foods, it was hardly taken as being valid, and therefore it only played a subordinate role in the development of food processing. In those days there were certain signs of the present development in the whole-food industry, but the only improvements that could be taken seriously were the rapid developments in deep-frozen foods. At the end of the sixties, I was very involved in this field and never gave it a second thought when I built a factory for canning, freezing and preserving fish.

The entire food industry had an insatiable appetite for better and more convenient products. Convenience or ready foods were the motto. Based on this motto, the last century, especially the last thirty years, brought a revolution in manufacturing, distribution and consumption. The progressive development, which has its roots in America, was initially so positive and future orientated that nobody doubted its validity. But unfortunately it was only a development that, until we reverse again, will create one of mankind's greatest challenges.

In actual fact, we are back to that well-known vicious circle. We are harvesting better-looking and bigger but manipulated crops from soil that is fertilized synthetically, but these crops are so weak that they have to be protected from weeds, insects and mildew with insecticides and pesticides. These crops, which are additionally polluted from the environment, go through automatic processing and are made into durable raw products. These processed raw foods undergo further processing and are then made available as end products. After these "raw products" have gone through various other processes such as being heated or treated with preserving agents or radiation, they end up in an attractive and luxurious packet. They can then be stored for longer or shorter periods (depending on the product). Then they are placed on the supermarket shelf, where they sit for months or even years without any particular care and are still offered for sale. After this odyssey, the end product finally reaches the consumer. According to its state the product will be stored for a further short or long period, and then begins its final torture. When "D-Day" arrives, it will be thawed out, heated up, processed further or booted through the microwave.

With the knowledge we have today about the negative side of food processing, it is obvious that we need to make changes in the food manufacturing industry. If we do not take the responsibility and decide to repair past mistakes, we will be guilty of blatant negligence or even of committing a crime. Crassly said, through the processing and manufacturing of unnatural foods we are guilty of bodily assault.

Mass-produced "partial food" nutrition or even the dead-energy carriers present just a tiny piece of a mosaic in the dramatic picture of modern mankind in today's industrial society.

Important Changes in the Farming Industry

All the promising experiments made by the farming industry, non-cultivation, synthetic fertilizers, pesticides and mass animal breeding have failed so miserably that the only logical step to take is an immediate changeover to a natural and traditional method of farming.

In recent years there has been some progress in so-called organic produce. Fruits and numerous processed products are actually enjoying a tremendous growth at good profit margins. However an organic processed product may be only slightly better than a processed non-organic item, which of course is confusing and misleading for the consumer. Furthermore there will not be certainty and secure standards even for organic fresh products until this is regulated by clearly defined international rules and laws.

A few essential counter-arguments for switching to regulated organic products will be:

A. With the traditional and natural means of cultivation and breeding of animals, it would not be possible to feed 6 to 7 billion (present world population).

B. Production would be expensive, and the products would be unattractive or unsightly.

C. It would take too many years to carry through such a change.

At first sight these counter-arguments appear credible and convincing, but let us take a closer look.

In view of the negative developments in the environment and the resulting threat to life on this planet, dramatic steps must be taken sooner rather than later. The sooner these steps are taken, the quicker will be the realization. It will only be possible to feed 6 billion people in a healthy way if the traditional natural methods of cultivation are enforced and a partial reduction in the consumption of meat and alcohol is made. Should the world population increase, it may be necessary to take the land that is presently used for raising cattle and growing sugar, coffee and cocoa to cultivate cereals, vegetables, fruits and nuts. Apart from this, there is much fallow land capable of cultivation. A combination of all these measures and greater research into natural fertilizers represents a great reserve that could even support and feed a moderate increase in the world population. However, a natural form of nourishment can only be achieved when the world population is controlled and steps are taken to improve the environment. There are measures that can be taken that would do away with the continuous damage to the environment and would, at the same time, represent a gain in the form of natural fertilizers, i.e., humus. If the flush mechanism of all toilets were changed so that the amount of water used was reduced and at the same time the excrements were gathered for manure, then we could kill three birds with one stone:

1. Preservation of the already diminishing water supplies.

2. A drastic reduction in waste water.

3. A gain in natural manure.

In China this system is being used successfully in many large cities. In one building, for example, with twenty-eight apartments, the excrement was pumped out of the underground tank once a month and then taken to a humus processing plant. As the technology for small biomass reactors advances, the installation of a small unit in private homes or apartment buildings, where the entire organic waste can be utilized, can in the future be a viable option.

Experiments have been made of very impressive toilet systems with and without vacuum pumps. These systems, which are successfully used in some homes, ships and airplanes, save at least 80 percent of the water. If this vacuum system was supplemented with a four-stage compact sewage plant, then domestic waste could be biologically processed on the premises and the solid leftovers could eventually be taken away and used in the processing of humus. This way, the public sewage system could be relieved of a great burden.

For this system, narrower pipes are needed (15 mm instead of 100 mm), which means they are ideal when renovating older houses. The manufacturer of these new toilets has already received permission from the Minister of the Interior in Schleswig-holstein, to carry out pilot projects, Economical Building—Norderstedt. Similar improved toilets are also starting to be more popular in North America, particularly in sensitive rural areas and on small islands.

There are equally good large-scale projects and proven products available in the U.S.A. and Canada, but without a change in policy or change in pricing for water and waste water, little will happen.

It is true that naturally grown products can be unsightly and the crops are smaller. Both these things, however, are not necessarily disadvantages. We have probably all had the same experience that the best looking fruits and vegetables are often the most tasteless and watery products. Therefore, nowadays, homegrown organic fruits and vegetables are being sold with increasing success, especially because the taste is much superior to that of "artificially" grown products.

At first glance small crops are a great disadvantage, but on closer inspection this is not important, firstly, because the loss is partly compensated for through the superior quality, and secondly, because we have enough possibilities to compensate through the cultivation of better yielding products and a reduction in the breeding and raising of animals. Furthermore, there is manifold waste from industrial processing. Today consumers are becoming more conscious of what they are eating, mainly due to the drastic changes in the food industry in America and Europe. With a more localized production, as in the old days, we can save at least 20 to 30 percent of the products that spoil or are thrown away and therefore are wasted. All these facts put together give us great reserves that we never even realized. Efficient, renewable energies, decentralized and independent of the grid, would enable people to grow their own quality products in their own greenhouses any time of the year and even any time of the day, wherever they may be.

In today's world we have big discrepancies; one part of the world seems to have abundance and another part is starving. Much available data indicates a waste of up to 50 percent in North America and Europe. The waste can occur at any stage a product goes through. During harvest, storage, processing, preparation of the meal and as leftover after the meal, there is waste. As with most areas of concern, conservation is the best pathway; this applies to energy in any form as well as to food products. This represents the largest opportunity to overcome present or future shortfalls in supplies.

The Conversion of the Food-Processing Industry

First of all, I would like to repeat that there are no processed foods that can replace fresh whole foods that have not been heated. To understand the difference, take a look at the "Classification of our Foods" by Professor Kollath.

The processed food industry must find a path back to more traditional methods that keep the foods from becoming refined and unnatural. With many products the conversion can be made without great investments.

The following list of foods could be converted to whole-grain products simply by changing the recipes.

- All bread products, such as white bread, toast, buns, waffles, muffins, brown bread, so-called whole-grain bread or black bread that is usually baked with about 50 to 80 percent whole-grain could be converted to whole-grain products by changing the recipes.

- All pastas, such as spaghetti, macaroni, all types of noodles, pizza, raviolis and pastries.

- All types of cakes and biscuits, and here the sweetening must be replaced with natural fruit sweeteners.

An important necessity in the manufacturing of all products is the fresh grinding of the grain directly before usage so that oxidation and the loss of vitamins can be prevented. Today there are many different grain mills on the market for every use and quantity so that every baker, hotel and factory could find the one suitable for their use. For the kitchen, manual grain mills are on offer for as little as $95, and there are automatic, high capacity ones for about $700 to $800. The average price range for a good, practical home-kitchen grain mill lies between $300 and $500.

Tinned fruits, vegetables, meat and fish are as inferior as long-lasting pastry products. Deep freezing, a method of instantly freezing fresh foods, is the best form of conservation and is therefore preferable to all others. Ready-to-serve frozen meals are not recommended as they are often processed for a long time before deep freezing.

Some products, such as meat, fish and certain vegetables, can also be air-dried or freeze-dried in an effective way that preserves most vitamins and vital substances.

The processing of oils and fats must be confined to cold-pressed oils and natural cold fats. Margarine should only be made out of cold-pressed oils and fresh eggs. Butter should preferably be cultured and only made from fresh milk. All milk products should be only cold processed.

All totally denatured products, such as refined sugar, extracted white flour, artificial fats, starches, proteins, flavouring, etc. and the products derived from these, including all sweets and chocolates, should in reality be banned. At least, a consumer tax could be put on them. This has been practised for many years in Denmark with sweets and chocolates.

As this range of products is mostly in the hands of monopolies, it is to be expected that there would be enormous opposition. Therefore, an enforcement of this ban is surely utopian in most countries. However, it could be included in the same group as alcoholic beverages, tobacco, coffee etc. and at the same time they should be heavily taxed.

All brewed beverages, including wine and beer, should be less taxed when they are organic and not processed by heating or by adding sugar or other denatured substances. Fermented vegetables such as sauerkraut should be sold fresh from the barrel. In this context, it is interesting to point out that according to Professor Kollath it is correct to label beer and wine as food. They are living products and are in every aspect whole foods. Beer should only be brewed under the conditions of the German "Reinheitsgebot" (law of purity). Beer that is heated up or brewed with the addition of preserving agents is inferior to a natural beer. A natural beer consists of only pure water, malt, hops and yeast. Methods in which alcohol has been adulterated should be forbidden or taxed heavily. In Canada there are a range of naturally brewed beers, which you can identify by carefully inspecting the labelling.

There is a range of other products, such as dried, flash-dried, freeze-dried, extract fruits, vegetables and cereals. The processing method determines whether a product can be recommended or not. In all cases, the date of production and the expiry date must be present and the storage instructions must be followed.

The reorganization of the farming industry will take years, especially when the soil has been laced with synthetic fertilizers, pesticides and other chemicals for many years. However, a medium-term changeover to traditional cultivation and animal breeding is possible and could start right away.

The biggest problem of the reorganization of the farming industry lies in the areas of monoculture crops. Most areas of cultivation have been treated with pesticides and are subsequently contaminated. A high percentage of fields are tilled with fodder maize, and although it is very difficult to grow other crops on this soil, it is possible. The management of toxic contaminated soil is even more difficult, and it could take many years to decontaminate the soil.

Although no country can be forced into such a reorganization, it is possible to lay down certain standards. Products that do not comply with these standards could then be taken off the international market. With laws that support these improvements, a faster changeover would be encouraged.

With the standardization of E.E.C. (European Economic Community/EU European Union), we have a perfect example of conflict that arises and the potential positive or negative outcome. The new standards for beer introduced in Europe were for a far inferior-quality product, a manipulated denatured beer. Until then most European countries were still brewing the majority of beers in a natural way without stabilizers, preservatives or pasteurization. After the introduction of the new standards, denatured beer is now allowed in Europe just like in the rest of the world. In Canada, both types are available. As stated before, it is therefore advisable to read the labelling carefully or to consult with the beer store.

To prevent manipulation of future international standards, we need strong lobbies. First, we should appoint a small international group of experts to lay down the standards for natural cultivation and processing. This has to be on a purely factual basis. To meet the requirements for such measures, it is clear that international agreements are necessary to prevent possible discord in the fields of competition. Nonetheless we can start implementing these changes in our own country now. The benefits to our health and the reduction in health care spending should be worth it.

It is conceivable that we could have general market regulations for the agricultural industry, just as they are within the E.E.C. In order to accomplish this there would have to be an international institution somewhat similar to the EU commission. An institution for international agriculture under the UN would also have the advantage of using common funds to help with all famines and other disasters worldwide. This institution could also steer the flow of natural fertilizers that should be distributed internationally.

A warning must be given when organizing such an extensive, bureaucratic machine to carry out these international duties. It would be necessary to have a governing body that could discipline and control the administration. In the framework of a reduction in military forces, enough suitable manpower could be made available for the functioning of such an administration. It might also be taken into consideration that out of all the armies worldwide, a "Freedoms Army" could be established to take over peacekeeping and all duties of this kind. This would be established in conjunction with the existing UN agencies.

A Change in the Methods of Marketing

Due to the necessary changes in the future food market, the emphasis will be on fresh foods, and this will bring an inevitable alteration in the methods of marketing. This change may lead to developments in many different directions. It is conceivable that the traditional weekly farmers' market could be expanded to a daily market, and it is also conceivable that the functions of these markets, in less populated areas, could be run by special grocery shops, as it was in the past before supermarkets became so popular. This, of course, depends on the supermarkets and their courage and timing to develop in other directions.

Conceivable also is a return to the corner store in which local products could be offered. It is also possible that there would be a certain fallback to trading between producer and consumer, as is common in many parts of the world. Often, in Canada, producers sell most of their products directly from their farms or hothouses or through home delivery of certain groups of products. We see these types of sales growing in popularity, even in big centres like Toronto, Montreal or Vancouver.

In those Western industrial countries in which milk products play such a large role, it would be necessary for the distribution of non-heated milk products to go back to the system of small, specialized dairies, which can provide a better service. Depending upon how the collection of the milk is organized, this would be possible under the management of the existing large dairies as long as the individual batches of milk are kept fresh and separated for immediate fresh consumption or as raw material for other organic milk and cheese products. Success depends on the dairy producers' willingness to take on the challenge.

At present consumers are becoming more conscious of what they are eating. The mass production of vegetables from large greenhouses and other methods of mass cultivation can only have a future if the consumer can get organic products and rely on quality. Supermarkets will only partially be able to respond in favour of this; therefore an opportunity exists to develop small fresh farms or markets regionally or locally, as explained in the Canada 2020 vision in Part One of this book. Fields and greenhouses used for the cultivation of vegetables made available for direct sale will play a growing role in the future. With lucidity and reliability they will attract all those consumers who are willing to pay a little more in order to get top-quality food in its freshest form. When supermarkets fail to exert enough effort in this direction, they can expect increased numbers of informed consumers to take this direction and find what they are looking for. Even if it initially only represents a small percentage of the business, there is a clear trend toward this type of direct dealing.

It would be the same in other sectors. A butcher or slaughter-house can ultimately keep the confidence of their better informed public only if they make sure that their supply comes from healthily bred animals and not from mass breeding and mass slaughtering. During the large supply crisis in the UK and Europe due to BSE and similar sicknesses, the consumption of meat products went down by more than 50 percent in some areas. This decline in sales actually triggered butchers to change their marketing strategy by advertising which farm their products would be coming from, etc., and the farm would be accessible to the public for visitation. Consequently a large portion of the business shifted from the super-markets back to the much more transparent smaller butchers. Consumption was drastically reduced but the quality was improved.

The baker who grinds his own grain and visibly bakes his bread in the store is equally experiencing a certain renaissance in several European countries. In the future, informed consumers will, for health reasons, be prepared to go "miles" for wholesome bread or prepare it themselves.

Summing up, we can see that a change in the processing of food and a change in the marketing of food go hand in hand. As health challenges for consumers grow and they become better informed, they will demand wholesome and healthy quality foods.
Eventually it will not be good enough to offer a so-called whole-grain bread that is full of chemicals, preservatives, etc. Once consumers are better informed and see the need for a better product for health reasons, they will demand whole-grain bread without all the agents that are hindering their well-being.

Environmental Pollution and the Various Possibilities of Reducing It

In my introduction I said that I would deal with all the essential problems of food supply and of the environment. I have a very important reason for starting with nourishment. The key to a healthy life lies in the food that we eat. Only when we bring our food back to its natural state can a certain chain reaction occur. To be able to produce healthy food, the farming industry must be reorganized to produce organic products. To produce food supplies to a high health standard, industrial processing must be kept to a minimum. This means that the food industry must also be reorganized. The institute or commission could take over the service of distribution and at the same time preserve and expand such branches as deep-freezing, fresh foods and other possibilities of fresh food preparation.

The abolition of most types of synthetic fertilizers, pesticides and insecticides is the first important step to take to relieve the products of unnatural substances and to improve our environment. By abandoning the present terrible forms of intensive animal breeding and converting back to normal mixed-farming methods with free grazing cattle, the environment and groundwater would be protected and the quality of meat would be higher and naturally healthier.

With these fundamental changes comes the next very important development. The consumer would then receive his products from the producer in a more or less natural, unprocessed form, which would mean a drastic reduction in manufacturing and packaging. This saves enormous amounts of energy as well as packing material. Again, the environment would benefit. Such decisive measures would challenge the public and create a basis for the readiness to re-think many different fields.

To save our environment and create a sustainable future, it is essential that the necessary steps are taken without delay. It is extremely important that all people involved are motivated in a positive way to take part in these changes. It would not be very sensible to start looking for scapegoats; we need sustainable solutions without allocating fault. We are not dealing with a class conflict but with a common fight for the existence and survival of our environment. New ways must be found so that agriculture, industry and businesses concerned can be supported financially and morally to find new, sensible and lucrative tasks where their expertise will be appreciated and required. These changes cannot happen overnight. A long-range restructuring plan will give ample time for the badly needed changes to occur. The idea of an economical model of the "Canadian Way of Life" as described in the first vision part can play an important part in the reform.

Even if we presently still see immense conflicts in some countries, overall there is a move towards peace. If we take the example of the EU, European Union, where nearly 500 million people are united in one economical and political block, there is only a very remote possibility of a war within these nations. In the past century the two big World Wars originated in Europe, and yet today another war in this area is unthinkable.

Large industries worldwide that are engaged in supplying the military with equipment and arms need to find other meaningful employment. When the Soviet Empire collapsed, this was the single largest area of industry. You can imagine what kind of a challenge it was for that society. Millions of people in the Soviet Union lost their jobs, and they are still struggling to get over it.

There are unlimited opportunities to utilize these idle industrial capacities for the necessary systems we will build for the relief of the environment. As pointed out in the Innovation section of this book, renewable energy, new transport systems and the redesigning of water and wastewater systems will create millions of jobs and provide meaningful employment for people who were manufacturing rockets, weapons and war machinery.

In the future, because of a change in world priorities, military expenditures can be drastically reduced. The financial savings would be enough to support industry in making these decisive reforms that will benefit the environment. Subsequently, I will be explaining a few ways in which these reforms can be carried out.

The Renewal of the Farming Industry—A Great Relief for our Environment

If these gigantic reforms are to be mastered, then the U.S.A., Canada, the administration for the European Market, all the farming institutions and the agricultural ministers for each separate country must participate.

Presently, the E.E.C. is engaged in a campaign to compensate every farmer who has fallow land. This compensation combined with other means could be given to the farmers to enable a changeover to traditional cultivation methods and the breeding and rearing of animals in the traditional way. This would of course mean considerably more manpower, and here is a chance to integrate the unemployed through retraining. Also, those of the manpower from the food industry who would lose their jobs through the changes could be re-employed in the modern farming industry.

A revival of smaller or even part-time farm units has its charm, and with new technologies and an abundance of renewable energy, organic farming on a year-round basis would be very attractive. Hothouses would be able to produce the majority of our fresh organic fruit and vegetables, making long distance shipping unnecessary. Products would be better quality, fresher, and the environment would be relieved.

With most synthetic fertilizers and pesticides abolished, there would be a noticeable improvement in agricultural products and in the soil. Apart from these improvements, there would be no further problems with sewage as a result of a reduction in the number of animals being kept and the abolition of mass breeding methods. A further burdening of the ground water would be eliminated, and the sewage waste could then be used with other natural fertilizers. To make this form of agriculture even more efficient and independent, all forms of energy would be contemplated and employed. Installations for solar energy, wind energy, some forms of biogas and other possibilities should be made more attractive and economical through mass production. Once these installations are a matter of course for every farm, there would be an abundance of energy and our environment would benefit tremendously.

It is not the objective of this book to condemn every "progressive step" that has been taken in the past. On the contrary, every practicality that is born out of the technical progress should be employed. However, an analysis of many farms would show that horses in many cases are more practical and rational than a tractor. They would save a great deal of energy and protect the environment and even be more pleasant and healthy (noise, air pollution and dust). *Co-operative* is not a foreign word for most farmers and could be a good option; e.g., the common ownership of equipment or other agricultural machines that are seldom used on a mixed farm.

With these revolutionary changes in the farming industry other possibilities come to mind. Smaller machines could be used economically and rationally, as they are in market gardens. Due to the special condition of the soil or because of other peculiar circumstances, there will be, without doubt, a need for special types of industrial-scale organic farms in the future, but they would be an exception to the rule. The negative aspects of the present intensive, one-sided farming industry could to some extent disappear again and make room for a revival of traditional mixed farms.

Reduction in Packaging Materials Would Lead to Huge Relief for the Environment

Nothing besides the automobile has changed the world so much as the packaging materials of our modern industrial society. The enormous mountains of waste of every kind are primarily caused through packaging.

There needs to be much rethinking in this sector. With the proposed changes to the farming industry, only a minimum of packaging materials would be necessary. The packaging sector of the manufacturing industry would then have to be reduced. Some recycled materials could be used, and it would be the responsibility of society to help. Hardly any other industry is so creative and has as much know-how as the packaging industry. Therefore it is of great worth to preserve and employ these talents so that more rational, more environmentally friendly and less encumbering forms of packaging can be found for the future.

The majority of all disposable packaging must be replaced with reusable glass bottles, jars, etc., or with containers the customer brings along. Good systems of reprocessing one-way glass can also drastically improve the situation. The laws must be changed so that all disposable packaging that only serves as a means of advertising or decoration will be highly taxed. This needs to apply to food, tobacco, confections and consumer articles of all kinds, including textiles, spare parts, etc., At the same time, an improvement in separating household recycling and waste disposal would further reduce the burden on our environment. A strict separation of all waste is very important. Organic waste, plastic, glass, and paper, etc. must go into individual containers according to the recyclable materials. In order to achieve this, it will be necessary to have an electronic system that continuously checks all containers being loaded on the garbage trucks. Containers that do not comply will be separated for manual work. The necessary manual sorting will then trigger fees, penalties for not obeying the rules, which will pay for the extra work.

To carry out all these changes it would be most important to have the public's support. Therefore education needs to play a major role. The information and the inspiration to be self-motivated must start with our youngest children through ECE and in primary school.

The above measures would lead to a reduction of up to 60 to 80 percent of waste products in all civilized countries. In the undeveloped countries a partially return to the traditional ways of life could be achieved sooner when monoculture crops have been abolished and a natural and balanced agriculture is put in place.

Cars, Trains, Airplanes, Ships and Other Methods of Transportation

Industrialization has brought a sensational development in methods of transportation. Nothing has had such an effect upon mankind as the possibilities that are associated with its mobility. This is true for all civilian and military sectors.

We have learned from long experience to appreciate the advantages of this freedom of movement. We must also admit that the present methods of transportation, especially the types of cars, trucks and airplanes presently in use, are unbearable menaces to our environment. It is not possible to imagine an existence without these methods of transportation, but we must find ways to take the burden off the environment without enforcing a drastic reduction of personal vehicles. We cannot delay the reduction of harmful substances that are being set free in the atmosphere worldwide; therefore we must also contemplate other methods of transport and traffic planning. The priority lies in the lessening of the burden in large cities and towns. The noise and the pollution that cars make have become intolerable. It is time that tangible concepts are developed that can be realized. In the same way, the automotive industry must be inspired to develop efficient, lighter, quieter and more modest cars. There are presently several car models designed with a consumption of 2 litres or less per 100 km. Why are they not available on the market? This would be realized when cars are taxed according to their petrol consumption and the amount of exhaust fumes they emit. This alone would bring a rapid change. However, ideally lightweight cars, trucks and trains will be fuelled by renewable energy. Efficient systems such as those proposed in the first part of this book will help to relieve the environment, create new industrial and economical opportunities and clean the air and water.

In respect to a new generation of lighter, quieter and more economical cars, other forms of energy will be available. From solar energy to hydrogen and vegetable oils, new fields of research wait to be explored in the future.

The aviation industry must also find new ways. The present pollution of the atmosphere is intolerable. As long as no other alternative incentives or other methods of energy can be found, an environmental tax should be enforced, to make flying less attractive. New international regulations must be worked out to ensure a relief of the burden on the atmosphere.

It is very important that the shipping industry also be renewed. By adding a lofty environmental tax on all forms of fuel, the shipping companies would, no doubt, return to the centuries-old method—sailing. The present technical know-how has made the building of sailing ships with speed and comfort very competitive.

Such vigorous, universal reforms would bring down the consumption of crude oil so radically that the need for large oil tankers would be diminished. Smaller oil tankers would have to be constructed using a massive sectional construction so that even serious damage would not cause any leaking of oil.

The above ideas and suggestions for ways in which we could reform our present transportation system only outline a fraction of the possibilities. There is so much technical knowledge and such a capacity in various sectors that, under the provision of the enforcement of international laws, nothing stands in the way of realizing the organization of very progressive transport systems. Fuel cell technology and other alternatives will also rapidly evolve.

I would like to emphasize that all these changes must be carried out in such a manner as not to bring industries or even countries into financial hardship. The aim is not to force businesses or countries into bankruptcy. Decreased global military spending and the establishment of international acts of preservation (e.g., establishing environmental consumer taxes) would provide large sums of money to solve any problems that might arise during the processes of reform.

Renewable Energy

Remarkable advances have been made in renewable energy in recent years. The biggest breakthrough in computer engineering was the development of a smaller microchip. There have been breakthroughs in all areas of renewable energy, but the most promising period for solar photovoltaic is in the immediate and mid-range future. Prices are already less than 10 percent of what they were a few decades ago. We expect a further reduction of 50 percent to 80 percent within the next three to five years. It is therefore crucial to participate and encourage development in this industry. Fuel cell technology and biomass reactors are also heading toward major breakthroughs. Wind energy is today's biggest winner and the fastest growing new energy source on earth and will hopefully also find its way to Canada.

In "Food for Thought," of course the primary emphasis is on food-related issues. However, all things are related and food is also energy, and that is an interesting aspect we should not forget.

The Abolition of All Unessential Chemicals

In total, more than 100,000 chemicals are used in industrial products including processed foods. Many of these products are certainly useful and harmless. However, in respect to nutrition, we have learned that every denaturing process in food production represents a danger to mankind. Therefore in food products the use of chemicals should be reduced drastically and monitored carefully. In all other products, they should only be used if it can be guaranteed that there are no side effects.

In each industry, regardless of what is manufactured, i.e., paint, plastic, food, etc., the use of chemicals should be thoroughly examined. The packaging manufacturing industry is responsible for the creation of millions of tons of garbage that arise each year. The complete range of plastics, chemicals and packaging is immense. It is a fact that mankind was able to live quite well without all these products and it is necessary to revert back to some of the previous methods. Without much hardship, ways can be found to live just as comfortably without excessive packaging, which will ensure a better way of life and maintain a comfortable standard of living.

The main problem lies in restructuring the present industry so that it can survive the initial period of transition and eventually build up new and sensible ways of employment. I am certain that such and similar measures are the basis for realizing all future projects of reform.

Chlorofluorocarbons and Other Similar Gasses

Everyone has heard of CFCs. The media has provided numerous reports on CFCs and their effect on the ozone layer. Although we have known the consequences of CFCs for many years, we are still using some products in which they can be found. On a positive note, most such sprays are no longer manufactured.

Nonetheless, new and similar products are being developed all the time and the consequences of these are not readily visible and may not be for years to come. Why are we not addressing the situation? Why don't we change to pump sprays? They are almost as convenient, are more economical to use and do not harm the environment. Instead the industry tries to convert to other gasses, which have not been fully tested, rather than stopping the production of gas sprays.

All Cleaners, Detergents and Disinfectants

There are many products that are extremely poisonous and dangerous for both human beings and the environment. They burden the water supply, our drinking water, water used for agriculture and subsequently for our food. Last but not least, they cause pollution and allergies of all kinds.

It is important to regulate this sector by enforcement of laws that leave no room for doubt. Only products that have a quick biological decomposition and that are not dangerous in any way to the environment and to mankind should be produced.

Electric Batteries

At the moment, throwaway batteries play a big role in the pollution of the environment. Only a small part of these are being disposed of in a correct manner. This is because most people are not aware of the problems involved or they are simply not interested, and so most old batteries are thrown away in the household bin. In actual fact the correct disposal of batteries is only partially possible.

In view of this it is necessary to enforce stringent laws to allow for 100 percent special disposal methods. To make this possible, only batteries that can be recharged should be sold. It might even be necessary to register all batteries.

The Disposal of all Non-biological, Non-decomposable Products

Previously I mentioned that by changing our way of life and our eating habits there would be a great reduction in the amount of waste/garbage that we produce. Additionally it is absolutely necessary to abolish the production of all products that burden the environment. It is irrelevant if these products are packaging, building materials or even textiles. To bring such useful regulations into force an analysis must first be made to ascertain the composting factors for all raw materials and products of mixed raw materials. Artificial chemical compounds should only be produced if a rapid biological composting factor is at hand. Exceptions should be allowed only for the period of reform, and even then the disposal methods must be kept safe. I am thinking of the fields of medicine and technology.

Chapter Fifteen

Connections Between the Environment, Nutrition, Hereditary Characteristics and Addictions

There is hardly a doubt that addictive illnesses can be directly connected with the environment, nutrition or with hereditary characteristics. A completely healthy, non-degenerated human being who lives in an intact world and benefits from whole-food nourishment could hardly be a candidate for drugs. Just as we cannot treat degenerative diseases without getting at the roots of the degeneration, we cannot treat addictions without finding the background cause.

We can try as much as we like, without any success, in our endeavour to treat addiction without first getting to the root cause. Good health is the basic foundation for a good and happy life,and this is only possible in a healthy, intact surrounding with natural healthy food and physical exercise.

Why are we so restless and so unbalanced? Why have we become so addicted? Obviously, we are addicted because we ignore the rules of creation or the rules of nature. We have destroyed our peace of mind and our natural environment through noise, dirt and stress. We have tried to subordinate nature with too much technology. The resulting de-natured products, poisoned water and filth in the atmosphere is making us ill and addicted.

233

Is it a wonder that more and more people are trying to escape and run away from reality? They are yearning for a peaceful and happy world and are longing for security and harmony. Therefore, in one way or another, we are all addicted without knowing it.

Our bodies cry out for vital substances that are not to be found in denatured processed foods. Our bodies are fighting against dirt, poison, noise and stress, and craving for exercise. The results are obvious: all kinds of physical and mental diseases. This creates a vicious circle from which most of us cannot escape. The longer we or the longer our ancestors have led such an unnatural way of life, the greater is the negative change in our genes. This is a very important point and accounts for the degree of degeneration in our health.

We are addicted to coffee, tea, alcohol and drugs, sugar, chocolate, white flour, etc. Being addicted has become a normal part of our lives. If somebody today is not addicted to any of these things, then he is considered abnormal. In the same way, being ill has also become a normal part of our lives. Everyone has his own general practitioner, his own ear, nose and throat doctor, his own optician, dentist, gynecologist, urologist, dermatologist, etc.

The degeneration of our bodies from eating modern processed foods is going into the fourth or fifth generation, with intervals of scarcity (for example, wartime). However these leaner, healthier periods, with less refined food and meat, during the last two World Wars brought only a slight relief in the development of the degeneration but not retrogression. A change back to a more natural way of life and a diet of whole foods without addictive drugs, coffee, tea, sweets etc., can be the only way to revoke this development. The weakened and ailing human being could be helped by a healthier diet, richer in vitamins and minerals, resulting in a stronger, well balanced and more harmonic being.

Even though the media tries to convince us that life would not be worth living without coffee, nicotine, sweets and ready-packed meals, and even certain drugs, the truth is actually reversed. Nourishment from whole foods would intensify the ability to fully appreciate and enjoy our food. Whole foods are in reality more intensive, of better quality, and there is much more creativity and diversification once we know how to prepare the enriched assortment of foods.

I have been through this development myself, as an average North-European and new Canadian. I know from my own experience all the weaknesses and strengths of this particular situation. I found trying to give up smoking was practically impossible without substitute drugs, such as sweets, resulting in a weight gain of ten to fifteen kilograms.

My friends and acquaintances kept telling me that the sum of the vice is the same. If you stop drinking coffee, you start drinking tea. As long as the body is in disharmony with itself due to eating denatured food or using drugs, any attempt to give up a certain addiction is only possible when substituting another for it. To this extent my friends were right. It was a stomach illness that forced me to consider things more seriously. My illness was due to an unnatural way of life and hereditary degeneration. I had a great deal of luck. Through my family and my connections with the food industry, I was able to get the right information and the necessary support to go new ways.

Our mental health is just as important as our physical health. The industrial age has created denatured foods and an unnatural, fast-paced lifestyle. Equally unnatural is the modern way of living and our relationships with each other. In the past, larger family units with several generations would live under one roof. People would help and support each other within the family and also within the greater society. Today in large cities loneliness and misfortune are abundant, leading more easily to such negative phenomena as drug addiction, sexual misbehaviour and crime.

Such a negative environment as it exists in anonymous societies is particularly threatening. Denatured nourishment, environmental pollution, stress and a lack of exercise create an ideal foundation for allergies and illnesses of all kinds. With these negative developments in mind, especially in respect to drug addictions, a long-term solution can follow only when we take all things into consideration. Only then do have we a real chance of getting at the roots of the trouble.

Already close to 10 percent of the North American population is addicted to drugs or medications, and the tendency is rising. The entire drug consumption costs more than food consumption, and when we take into consideration the consumption of softer drugs like coffee, nicotine, alcohol etc., then food ends up at the bottom of the list. According to the White House Office of National Drug Control Policy Fact Sheet, in the year 2000 there were in the U.S.A. 15.9 million users of illicit drugs alone. This does not include the millions of addicts of prescription drugs. The illicit drug costs were between U.S. $64.8 and 80 billion and estimated additional cost to society U.S. $160.6 billion totally approximately U.S. $240 billion a year (www.whitehousedrug policy.gov/publications/factsht/drugdata/index).

When one reads these shattering statistics from North America, Europe and Asia,we can be certain that this development will be introduced on a similar scale into all the other highly civilized countries of the world and gradually even into underdeveloped countries. These terrible problems with drug addictions stand side by side with those of environmental pollution, unnatural and unhealthy nourishment, lack of physical exercise and other issues of the modern civilization. They are the greatest challenges mankind has ever faced. If we want to survive, then we must fight against these basic evils with all our might and go back to natural form!

Considering the seriousness of drug addiction and pollution, the problems caused by nicotine, alcohol, coffee and sweets, etc., seem to lose their significance, and we are tempted to put them at the bottom of the list. However, the key to a healthy life lies in every drop of clean water, every breath of clean air and every healthy grain of corn, and it would be a great mistake to separate these problems.

When we agree to follow the universal laws of nature, there will be a chance of stopping this very negative development. Is this enough to save our planet? I do not know. It is very difficult to judge. Being an optimist, I do believe it is never too late to reverse things; it will only be a matter of time. Looking at all aspects in this optimistic light and using all our energy and all the means at our disposal, the chances could look good.

How I Experienced the Change in My Life

I think it is very important to say that it was a simple bit of knowledge that changed and influenced my life in such a positive way. No wonder drug or new medicine, no clever medical apparatus or wonder healer. Not one of these things. It was merely the recognition and guidance given by following the rules of nature that led me into a normal, naturally happy life.

Just like any other average consumer, I used to be a regular visitor to the doctors. At first my stomach ailments could be treated successfully, for at least short periods of time, by eating a strict diet and taking antacid tablets. The recommended diet consisted usually of so called "bland foods," dead and boiled denatured foods such as rusks, boiled milk soups, potato puree, etc. With such a diet it is quite astonishing that there were even short periods of improvement in my health, but this was most likely due to my "spirit" and the usual peace and quiet that is always prescribed in such cases.

Later on, the new "acid blockers" came on the market. This medicine, which blocks the acid production of the stomach and really does bring relief, has, however, very bad side effects. It can affect hormone production; that means that a male patient can eventually grow breasts. Additionally, the medicine can cause a lazy bowel, resulting, of course, in further treatment with purgatives. Even when this medicine brings more or less relief, one can always reckon on setbacks. In other words, there is no real recovery without a healing process. Eventually I became seriously ill, and after years of suffering, my long-time doctor friend urgently proposed major surgery to overcome what had evolved into a cancerous situation. In this very threatening situation, I was forced to decide which way to go. I was given the choice to remove most of my stomach and replace it with tissue taken from the intestine. I had heard about this method. It causes suffering and one of the resulting difficulties is that the intestinal tissue used to replace your stomach struggles to process enough food to keep you alive. The more I heard about it the less appealing this sounded to me so I looked for other alternatives. Considering all the pros and cons, I determined that I wouldn't really lose anything by trying out something different.

I did hear and read a lot about fasting, meditation, homeopathy, salt-free cooking, clean drinking water, whole foods, and much more. I had long conversations with my daughter Andrea, who as a teen already had strong views about the negative effects of refined foods, including the type of foods my company mainly was involved in producing and marketing at that time. Some of it was initially difficult for me to accept. However the more people I consulted and the more I thought this through, the more it made sense that detoxification, wholesome foods and a healthy lifestyle probably would be the right pathway for my future.

I ventured out in this direction, and the first partial recovery came as a miracle. After a fasting period allowed me to completely detoxify, I changed to whole foods, and after stopping all medication, I experienced an amazing change in my overall well-being.

Whenever we want to change or improve our lives, we must understand that a situation like an illness, particularly when we are speaking about a chronic condition, usually takes a long time to develop. Therefore it should not be surprising that it also takes a long time to cure it.

This was the beginning of my cure. It took quite a long time and would positively change my life into something I had never envisioned would be possible.

Young and critical readers might say, this has nothing to do with me, for although I eat modern processed foods I feel fit and healthy. The reaction is understandable; they have not personally experienced the decay that slowly and gradually sneaks into our bodies after eating refined foods over a longer period of time. However, the fact is that, apart from the existing hereditary damage, after about twenty years of consuming these foods a young person will suffer exactly the same or similar types of ailments as I did. It is therefore of great importance that in younger years children will be given a knowledge and awareness of this. In fact, it would be reasonable to start with this in kindergarten and primary school.

My change to vegetarian whole-food nourishment gave me a wonderful feeling of relief, especially since I could eat as much as I wanted, and at the same time, I stopped smoking without putting on weight. I had a feeling of vitality and cleanliness. Most of all I noticed that by eliminating meat from my diet, stomach acid was reduced, resulting in an unknown, agreeable feeling of youth and harmony.

The most astonishing experience I had was that because I was eating a whole-food diet, I had absolutely no yearning for meat. On the contrary, at the beginning I developed a certain aversion to meat. Later on this aversion was not so intensive, but meat lost all its attraction for me, although I sometimes eat small amounts of fresh seafood. Today, after being a vegetarian for almost thirty years and having totally recovered from two major chronic illnesses in my life, I have regained my health completely, and as a sixty-two year old my energy level is better than it has been in decades.

Chapter Sixteen

A Practical Guide for Changing Over to Whole Foods

Recommended Kitchen Utensils:

- household mill with grinding stones
- germinating apparatus for germinating different grains, nuts and beans
- stainless steel grater or kitchen mixer with grater for preparing salads
- electric coffee grinder for grinding nuts, flaxseed, etc.
- pepper mill and lemon press
- mincing knife for cutting kitchen herbs
- weighing scales and measuring beaker
- draining bowl or colander

Shopping List to Establish a Stock of Raw Foods (Organic):

- wheat, rye and oats (1 to 2 kg, or even better, prepackaged wholesale bags of 10 to 20 kg)

- raw nuts, such as hazelnuts, almonds, walnuts, sunflower seeds, cashew nuts and pine nuts (when possible, fresh)

- cold-pressed vegetable oil, such as thistle, olive or sunflower seed oil

- fruit vinegar, such as apple cider vinegar (organic and natural—not heated)

- small lemons, onions, peppercorn and other spices, including garlic and flower pollen

- potatoes and unpolished brown rice

- whole-grain bread (without preserving agents and without any addition of white flour), fresh ground and fresh baked—this only applies if you do not buy the mill to bake your wholegrain bread, whole-grain crackers, whole-grain toast or whole-grain muesli toast, etc.

- kitchen herbs (fresh daily whatever is available and preferably in season)—parsley, chives, dill, chervil, basil, rosemary, caraway seeds, paprika, etc.)

- fresh apples, fresh fruit and vegetables, and fresh lettuce

- fresh butter (made out of unpasteurized milk)

- all kinds of teas, e.g., green tea, fruit tea, rosehip tea, lime blossom tea, peppermint tea, and so on.

For preparing meals and drinks you will need good quality tap water, and when this is not available, low-mineral-content water or table water. Most Canadian and U.S.A. tap water is surface water that contains a lot of unwanted substances and a high level of chlorine. This water needs to be filtered or put through reverse osmosis. Reverse osmosis is the best solution. A small system to be installed under your kitchen sink represents an investment of about $500, which is much cheaper than buying spring water and gives you a healthy supply of water for inside and outside your home.

All products dealt with here should preferably be organic. At present it is still difficult to obtain certain organic products. As awareness increases, organically grown produce and other products will eventually gain market share and also become more reasonable in price.

Although I did mentioned earlier in my book that a diet with whole foods and meat is possible, I am leaving all milk products (except butter), meat, poultry, fish and eggs off the list. I have done this because I am distinctly trying to point out how incompatible some of these products, and particularly milk, really are for a large part of our population. However, to make the changeover a little easier for you, I will make a few exceptions.

Important Vitamins and Minerals

Vitamin A: Found in carrots, green and yellow vegetables, butter, whole milk and egg yolk.
Effect: Stamina, growth, thyroid gland, and formation of hair, nails and teeth.

Vitamin B1: Found in whole fresh grains, nuts and yeast.
Effect: Digestion, growth and fertility.

Vitamin B2: Found in whole fresh grains, yeast, green vegetables, milk and eggs.
Effect: Clear skin, digestion and growth.

Vitamin B3: Found in whole fresh grains, yeast, green vegetables, eggs and milk.
Effect: Building up of brain cells and prevention of infection.

Vitamin B5: Found in whole fresh grains, nuts, eggs and cheese.
Effect: Important for all bodily functions and for red blood corpuscles.

Vitamin B6: Found in whole fresh grains, mushrooms, bananas and vegetables.
Effect: Stamina.

Vitamin B12: Found in whole fresh grains, soya beans, yeast and milk.
Effect: Red blood corpuscles and the nervous system.

Folic Acid: Found in raw vegetables, lettuce and walnuts.
Effect: Building up of the blood and nervous system.

Vitamin C: Found in fresh fruit and vegetables.
Effect: Stamina, digestion, detoxification and healing processes.

Vitamin D: Found in sunshine, cod liver oil, eggs and milk.
Effect: necessary for the intake of calcium and for building strong bones.

Vitamin E: Found in wheat germ, nuts and vegetables.
Effect: The building of cells and their maintenance.

Vitamin K: Found in green-leafed vegetables.
Effect: Essential for blood coagulation.

Calcium: Found in nuts, grain, green vegetables and milk.
Effect: For the building of bones and teeth.

Iron: Found in beans, dried fruits and vegetables.
Effect: For the building of red blood corpuscles.

Zinc: Found in whole fresh grain, seeds and onions.
Effect: For regulating vitamin A and the building of enzymes.

All vitamins and mineral substances can be found in adequate quantities in fresh, vegetarian foods. Milk and eggs have only been included to round off the list. Other animal products are not included because the vitamins are mainly found in the sweet meats and organs, which are contaminated anyway from environmental pollution.

Food Categories established by Professor Kollath

	Whole-food		Processed food		
a) natural	b) changed mechanically	c) changed by fermentation	Heated	Preserved	Prepared
Seeds, nuts, almonds	Oils	Yeast bacteria	Bread	Cakes, pastry	Vegetable preparation, artificial fat,
Seeds, grain	Ground products, whole flour, bruised grain	Raw porridge, whole bruised grain	Cooked porridge	Cakes with long shelf life sweets, chocolate	starch, egg white, refined sugar, extracted flour, semolina, noodles
Fruit	Salad, naturally cloudy juices	Fermented juices	Fruit	Fruit cans, jams	Aroma, fruit sugar,
Vegetables	Salads	Fermented vegetables, sauerkraut	Vegetables	Canned vegetables	vitamins, ferments, nutrient salt
eggs	blood	Raw mincemeat	Heated meat	Canned meat	Prepared animal products
milk	Milk products	Fermented milk	Cooked milk	Canned milk	Canned milk
Spring water	Tap water	Fermented drinks, wine, beer	Extracts, tea, bouillon	Mixed drinks, artificial wine, liquor	Distillates, artificial mineral water, brandy

Chapter Seventeen

Important Information About Our Basic Nutritional Substances

Protein/Amino Acids

In our westerly, civilized nutrition, there is a considerable over-supply of protein. The World Health Organization has suggested that a daily intake of 33 grams of protein is sufficient for a person weighing seventy kilograms. This requirement can easily be obtained from portions of cereals and vegetables in our diet.

Breast milk contains approximately 2 percent protein, which is about 5 percent of the calories we need per day. W.H.O. recommends 33 grams = 4.5 percent for an adult. Most cereals and vegetables have at least 10 percent of calories in form of proteins. For example, wheat has 17 percent, oats 15 percent, vegetables about 10 percent, potatoes 11 percent and cabbage more than 20 percent. If we eat only the above-named foods, we would be getting more than double the protein that we need.

We must realize that our digestive system can only convert fresh or live amino acids into digestible protein. Commonly known is the fact that if our temperature is raised, such as by a fever, we get to a critical stage when our body temperature is higher than forty-one centigrade. This is mainly because our body

247

proteins will "die" when the temperature increases further. The colour of meat being cooked changes from pinkish to gray or white and signals the conversion.

Food scientists have found that the ability to digest and utilize proteins is increasingly reduced the longer we heat the meat or food. Therefore when we eat heated fish, meat or milk products, we lose the greater part of the proteins through heating. This protein can be an additional burden to our kidneys, since it has to be filtered through the kidneys and excreted in our urine. This is a terrible waste in three ways:

1. The expenditure of producing protein through red meat is about fifteen times as high as producing vegetable proteins.

2. If our bodies can only absorb about two-thirds of the total worth of the food that we eat, consider the extreme impact this constitutes for the national economy in the western hemisphere: of the 1,000 million people living here, with an average yearly household food budget (three people) of $3000, this makes a total of about 330 million households times $1000 thousand = $330 billion. Taking the rest of the world into consideration with the same sum of money, then we reach a total of $660 billion. Of this, two-thirds is a complete loss, as it does nothing to sustain us. In addition, we must not forget the costs arising from diseases originating from this type of diet, which could potentially be in the region of another few hundred billion dollars per annum.

3. Osteoporosis can be closely related to the eating of animal proteins. The lack of calcium, which affects all women and is particularly conspicuous in older women, is due in part to eating animal proteins that cause a rise in the requirement of calcium. For years now, attempts have been made to balance this requirement by giving calcium supplements, without great success.

These sensational allegations are of such importance that I would like to present a couple of independent scientific studies on this subject. They all prove the same thing (see Study No. 5). The more protein our bodies take in, the greater is the loss of calcium and the less healthy our bodies become. This process is similar to that of eating refined sugars. The digestion of refined sugars deprives the body of vitamin B, and this has devastating results and causes acute illnesses and symptoms of degeneration.

Osteoporosis

Is this disease caused by a lack of calcium or by eating too much animal protein?

Five different studies from five competent American scientists have clearly shown that nourishment rich in protein (such as meat, milk products, eggs or concentrated vegetable proteins) leads to a lack in calcium, even when additional calcium is given in large doses. These same studies prove that under the same circumstances a normal vegetarian diet, also called "poor protein" diet, leads to a surplus of calcium. A diet of fresh vegetarian foods (nuts, seeds and green vegetables) contains more valuable calcium than milk products.

For more detailed information on these studies refer to the following resources:

Study No. 1
C. Anad, "Effect of protein intake on calcium balance in young men given 500 mg daily." Journal of Nutrition 104:695, 1974.

Study No. 2
M. Hegsted, "Urinary calcium and calcium balance in young men as affected by level of protein and phosphorus intake." *Journal of Nutrition* 111:53, 1981.

Study No. 3
R. Walker, "Calcium retention in the adult human male. As affected by protein intake." *Journal of Nutrition* 102:1425, 1970.

Study No. 4

N. Johnson, "Effect of level of protein intake on urinary and fecal calcium and calcium retention in young adult males." *Journal of Nutrition* 100:1425, 1970.

Study No. 5

H. Linkswiler, "Calcium retention of young adult males as affected by level of protein and calcium intake." *Trans New York Academy of Science* 36:333, 1974.

Study	Extra calcium intake In mg.	Change in the calcium retention	
		Poor Protein Diet	Rich Protein Diet
1.	500	+31	Minus 120
2.	500	+24	./. 116
3.	800	+12	./. 85
4.	1,400	+10	./. 84
5.	1,400	+20	./. 65
Average	920	+19	Minus 94

These examples once again prove that the science of nutrition is still in the beginning stages. Additional doses of minerals and vitamins are sometimes helpful, but the problem as a whole must be dealt with. As a first step in any medical treatment, a suitable whole-food diet should be prescribed. This alone can prevent deficiencies and illness.

There is also an important connection between the production of acid and calcium. Osteoporosis is caused when the blood contains too much acid, in other words, when the pH is too high. An over-acidity of the blood arises from eating too many animal products, which are acid forming. Most vegetable food is alkaline and therefore has no negative influence on the pH levels.

When the acid level in our blood rises too high, we die. Therefore, to compensate for high pH levels in the blood, the body takes calcium from the bones. Because calcium is alkaline, the acid level starts to fall. This means, of course, the greater the consumption of animal products, the greater the loss of calcium in our bodies.

It is therefore almost impossible for a vegetarian to suffer from osteoporosis. Those who do are usually revealed as being lacto-ovo-vegetarians who eat large quantities of eggs and milk products or those who are known as pudding-vegetarians who eat a one-sided or inferior diet. A normal whole-food vegetarian, who enjoys a mixed diet of cereals, vegetables, nuts and fruits, is the only one who would rarely suffer from this disease.

It is worth mentioning that additional doses of calcium can only be given when supplemented with doses of phosphor and vitamin D.

Fat

International fat consumption statistics (see page 255) clearly show that the consumption in Northern Europe and North America is 140–160 grams daily, much higher than the normal average. Additionally, the type of fat consumed is significant as animal fat puts a bigger strain on the body. Countries with a lower fat consumption (20–60 grams) also show a higher consumption of vegetable fat as opposed to animal fat.

For years now, scientists have been arguing about the role cholesterol (in animal fats) plays in the many civilization diseases. The negative influence of animal fats is even greater due to an unhealthy change in our metabolism, which is a result of denatured foods. Therefore, the consumption of animal fats would not have the same fatal consequences for someone who normally eats whole food compared to someone who eats dead-energy carriers. Nevertheless, there is no doubt that the consumption of any type of animal product (meat, eggs, milk, sour-milk products, cheese and butter) is quite dangerous to our health, simply because of the high concentration of saturated fatty acids.

Even more dangerous and complex are those so-called *trans fatty acids*. Whole books could be written about the disastrous impact these have on our health. The attached FDA fact sheet about TFA gives us a simple but helpful overview.

FDA FACT SHEET
WHAT EVERY CONSUMER SHOULD KNOW ABOUT
TRANS FATTY ACIDS
JULY 9, 2003

Q: What *are* trans fatty acids?
A: Trans fatty acids (or "trans fat") are fats found in foods, such as vegetable shortening, some margarines, crackers, candies, baked goods, cookies, snack foods, fried foods, salad dressings, and many processed foods.

Q: Why should I care about trans fat?
A: It's important to know about trans fat because there is a direct, proven relationship between diets high in trans fat content and LDL ("bad") cholesterol levels and, therefore, an increased risk of coronary heart disease—a leading cause of death in the US.

Q: Aren't *all* fats bad?
A: No. There are "good" fats and "bad" ones, just like there's good and bad blood cholesterol. Saturated fats and trans fat have bad effects on cholesterol levels. Polyunsaturated fats and monounsaturated fats (such as olive oil, canola oil, soybean oil, and corn oil) have good effects.

Q: How much trans fat is too much?
A: There is research currently underway to determine this. However, it is true and accurate to say that the less saturated fat, trans fat and cholesterol consumed, the better. Trans fat, while pervasive in many of the foods we eat, is not "essential" to any healthy diet.

Q: How can consumers know if a product contains trans fat if it's not identified on the nutrition label?
A: Consumers can know if a food contains trans fat by looking at the ingredient list on the food label. If the ingredient list includes the words "shortening," "partially hydrogenated vegetable oil" or

"hydrogenated vegetable oil," the food contains trans fat. Because ingredients are listed in descending order of predominance, smaller amounts are present when the ingredient is close to the end of the list.

Q: Do restaurants have to list the fat content of their foods?
A: No. But it's a good tip to always ask which fats are being used to prepare the food you order.

Q: Why is it important to read labels?
A: Labels provide valuable information. An informed consumer is able to make better, healthier choices. So better labels make for smarter, healthier consumers.

Only cold-pressed oil contains vital fat-soluble vitamins and unsaturated fatty acids. Raw milk, from which butter or other products are made, also contains small amounts of essential unsaturated fatty acids. Therefore, a very moderate amount of these products can be eaten but only when the consumer is healthy and enjoys a whole-food diet. One should not forget that cow's milk is not meant for human consumption, even though it is high in value. It is meant for calves, and they have four stomachs and in less than fifty days after birth double their weight. It really does not matter whether arteriosclerosis is caused by unhealthy change in the metabolism due to denatured foods or because of the high degree of cholesterol in animal fats. Arteriosclerosis is the result of too much cholesterol in the blood, and this is the result of a large consumption of saturated fatty acids.

Shocking Facts about Cancer

The statistics on causes of death are obvious, but I would just like to add a few more important facts.

All research into the cause of cancer confirms the suspicion that these growths (e.g., the changes in the cells that take place in most types of cancer) can be directly connected with poor nutrition. Not included are the types of cancer caused by burdens put on the cells, such as repeated overdoses of sunrays, etc.

For years now, hundreds of billions of dollars have been spent on cancer research without bringing any real progress in treatment. If cancer is located early enough, it is possible to cure this with surgery, although the surgery is often drastic, such as the removal of breast, uterus, fallopian tubes, stomach, intestines, or prostate. Furthermore, some cancers can be treated by chemotherapy and radiation therapy. However it is questionable to what extent these therapies are truly effective or if those patients who survive this radical treatment would have survived anyhow.

Many studies have been done by well-known and reputed scientists all over the world that clearly indicate that most types of cancer are caused by long-term incorrect nutrition and lifestyle. The research done by Dr. Takeshi Hirajama was the largest study of this kind in the history of medicine, from the National Cancer Research Institute of Japan. This was done in the seventies and included over 120,000 participants. The results were convincing but at the same time startling.

Breast Cancer and Meat Consumption

With daily consumption of meat, in women the risk of developing breast cancer is four times as high. With a consumption of meat two to four times a week, the risk is tripled. With a consumption of less than once a week, there is no measurable risk.

Breast Cancer and Egg Consumption

With daily consumption of eggs, in women the risk of developing breast cancer is tripled. With egg consumption two to four times a week the risk is doubled. Only by consuming eggs less than once a week, is there no measurable risk.

In respect to milk products, the results are similar. Apart from this, American and English research had nearly identical results regarding cancer of the womb and of the fallopian tubes.

The most common cause of death in civilized countries are heart diseases, cancer and strokes.

The following are statistics from "Shocking Facts About Cancer." The relationship between these illnesses and the customary eating habits are quite obvious, as one can see in the following graphic:

Cause of death	Europe/U.S.A. approx. in %	South America approx. in %	Asia approx. in %
Heart diseases	38%	15%	10%
Cancer	18%	8%	6%
Apoplectic fits (Stroke)	11%	6%	5%
Fat consumption daily In grams	140 – 160	50 – 60	20 – 40
Meat consumption Per annum in kg	90 – 100	30 – 40	10 – 20

There are similar figures in respect to cancer of the stomach and cancer of the prostate. In countries where there is a high consumption of animal fats, nearly 50 percent of the men over sixty years of age are suffering from an enlarged prostate. Half of these cases result in cancer and about 10 percent result in death.

Up until now it was a common belief that cancer of the lung was caused primarily by smoking and other outside risks. Even if smoking very often is the root cause, there are indications that vegetarian smokers seldom suffer from this type of cancer. This means that the relationship to nutrition plays an important role.

The picture is becoming clearer. Cancer is definitely strongly linked to unhealthy diets, including the extensive consumption of animal products. This in combination with hereditary disease, smoking and other environmental influences and lack of exercise are probably the main reasons for cancer being able to evolve.

The question is, why does the medical profession or the government not react to these disconcerting findings? Is this field already so commercialized that disengagement is impossible because of the economic considerations?

We are surely just as much at the beginning of cancer research as we are in the research into nutrition. Perhaps we are already at the end, as we seem to be going around in circles. Due to industrialization of food production, denatured foods were developed, and the standard of living improved. That made a larger consumption of even greater amounts of animal products affordable. On one hand, technology and the consequent high standard of living has brought us many wonderful things. On the other hand, we have lost our natural balance due to our lack of exercise and our unnatural way of living.

Cancer can only be cured when we accept the facts, when we understand the mistakes made in the development of processed foods, the way we treat our environment and when we take the necessary actions. It is, of course, extremely difficult to give up bad habits, and it is therefore necessary that we use every opportunity to inform the public of the facts. Education in nutrition should be introduced as soon as possible, starting with children in kindergarten and primary schools.

Carbohydrates

Foods that contain carbohydrates are the most important sources of energy for human beings as they are made up of starches and sugars in their natural form. They are present in cereals, fruits and vegetables, and they are easy to digest and wholesome.

When we only take in isolated carbohydrates, the consequences are fatal. These are primarily found in refined sugar or extracted white flour, but we need to keep in mind that they are hidden in thousands of products like cakes, biscuits, breads, confectionery, etc. The result is that the body is deprived of vitamins that are essential for the digestion. This lack of vitamins brings the well-known feeling of hunger because the body is craving for a more wholesome diet with more minerals and vitamins.

Herein lies the simple explanation of why people who eat whole foods are slim and healthy. Only a diet of denatured foods brings overweight and its terrible consequences.

Since I changed my eating habits, I have paid much more attention to what other people consume. I have made the observation that nobody who eats a whole-food diet ever gets fat. There may be cases due to illness, but I have not yet met one. On the other hand, there are very few people in our prosperous society who don't have weight problems from eating a regular diet of isolated carbohydrates. Only people who live healthy lifestyles, who eat properly and who are physical active in some sort of sport can keep healthy and keep their weight under control.

I can only advise everyone to save themselves the torture of fighting obesity with miracle diets. It is better to do something that will be of a lasting effect, starting with eliminating products in which sugar or extracted white flour is used. A reduced intake of animal protein and fat and an emphasis on wholesome fruit, vegetables, legumes, nuts and cereals will bring the best results.

Even if the first step is difficult, after a short time you will see that a consequential changeover is not as terrible as you imagined. Your body is receiving all the vital minerals and vitamins it needs, and you will not have that sickly feeling of hunger. Half-hearted efforts are only partial efforts and usually give no satisfactory results. The consistent lack of vitamins and minerals will continue to cause that feeling of hunger until you have had a longer period of proper foods.

In summary, a whole-food diet is the key to a healthy way of life. These products carry the necessary proportions of proteins, fats, starches, sugars, minerals and vitamins that we need to ensure a healthy and fulfilling life.

Vital Substances and Mineral Salts

This category consists of the unsaturated fatty acids, all vitamins, trace elements, enzymes, all so called ballast substances and flavourings. The most important salts are sodium, calcium and magnesium.

An adequate supply can only be guaranteed when a balanced diet of mixed foods is taken. This exists in the form of germinated grains, fresh fruits, vegetables and nuts. These pure diets of vegetarian foods are sufficient and ensure a complete utility of our food. There are more than one billion vegetarians who can do without any animal products.

A vegetarian menu can, of course, be supplemented with eggs and milk products. The compatibility of these products is varying. Both have a high content of cholesterol, and milk, apart from the fact that it is a natural food for calves, after being heated up is a denatured food and therefore inferior. Vegetarians who have grown up with the massive advertising campaigns and propaganda from our meat, milk and egg producers are often worried that they cannot get along without milk and eggs, etc. Many ancient native tribes of this world have been living a healthy life for thousands of years without ever consuming meat, milk or eggs.

Of course there are also many essential minerals and vitamins in animal products. But animal products are only valuable and healthy when they are compatible. Once again one must differentiate between whole foods and inferior denatured foods. Heated milk products (and today that means nearly all milk products apart from superior first-rate milk and butter made out of fresh unpasteurized milk) are unfortunately only denatured foods. Milk that has neither been heated nor processed in any other way is of course very valuable to people who can tolerate milk. Today it is quite difficult to buy raw fresh milk due to the laws and regulations for food products. According to these, it is necessary to heat up and process milk to make it safe and edible for the consumer. If there was more attention paid to hygiene on farms and the further processing and distribution were not carried out on such an excessive basis, it would be possible to offer products made from fresh unheated milk. The present distribution of fresh milk, which at the moment is carried out on a small scale, proves this. Mankind has been drinking unheated milk for centuries without endangering its health, before the industrial food production evolved it into its present form. Due to the present excellent refrigeration and cooling methods and the supervision in respect to the durability of a product, it must be easier than ever. The key lies exclusively in the methods of animal breeding and keeping. Healthy animals that have not been confronted with an unnatural setting and treated with antibiotics or hormones produce healthy milk.

The same goes for meat products. A filet steak is similarly inferior as extracted white flour or sugar. When all parts of the animals are consumed in a fresh and raw state, it can be considered as a whole food. Excessive cooking destroys the proteins, whether they are of animal or vegetable origin.

In summary, the way in which the animals are kept and fed determines if meat is a high quality and wholesome food. Even a well-balanced amount of vitamins and minerals depends on this. It has been proven that people can live happily when eating vegetarian foods. Everyone who changes over from a mixed diet to a pure vegetarian diet is surprised how tasty, varying and digestible this is. When one experiences this, then there is always an increase in the desire for quality.

However, if you really cannot resist eating meat, then you must remember that an excessive consumption of such is a risk to your health. Greater care should also be taken in the quality of the product. In all cases it is advisable to cut the consumption of animal products drastically and to increase the consumption of high-fibre-content products (ballast foods) and fresher and more wholesome vegetables products.

A diet that consists of many animal products is not compatible with good digestion. For proper digestion to occur we need essential substances that can only be found in cereals, vegetables, nuts and fruits. The sequence and the combination of food intake is also of great importance. The intervals in the digestion process and the energy required also plays an important role. Because of the importance of these interrelations, I will be writing about them in more detail.

Chapter Eighteen

Losing Weight Without Hunger Pains and Resignation—Made Easy—Without Negative Results

Eating foods in the right succession is important and good for the digestion.

There is a very interesting basic rule that is of great importance to everybody but particularly to people who are overweight. As mentioned previously, the lack of vitamins and minerals caused by a one-sided diet of denatured foods brings a constant feeling of hunger. This hunger is then usually replenished by eating more of these unnatural and inferior foods, which eventually leads to obesity.

To break this vicious circle, one only has to go back to eating natural food and, more importantly, food we were meant to eat. This means a well-balanced mixed diet of preferably organic cereals, nuts, fruits and vegetables of all kinds. These products, if possible, should be eaten fresh and raw or only cooked briefly. It is impossible to become overweight with this kind of food intake. One can eat as much as the heart (stomach) desires of any of these foods, because due to an abundance of minerals and vitamins the feeling of hunger quickly goes away. Raw foods also need more chewing, and one has a feeling of being full even before the require-

261

ment of calories has been fulfilled. All this leads to an easy step-by-step way of getting rid of extra weight.

Usually changing to a mixed whole-food diet leads to a weight loss of five to ten pounds in the first few weeks. This process slows down somewhat but continues until the ideal weight is reached. Then a phase of stabilization begins. For me the process took more than a year. I felt full and satisfied after each meal and had stopped smoking at the same time. I lost about twenty kilograms (height 1.92 m; weight before 100 kilograms). Eighty kilograms is actually underweight for someone of my height, and it did in fact take another two years and a lot of physical exercise before I could put on another three kilograms to reach my ideal weight of eighty-three to eighty-five kilograms. Before I started eating a whole-food diet, this amount would have taken only a few days to put on and many months to get rid of it. I have now held my weight for many years, and in addition I have got back much of my youthful vitality.

The Importance of Food Combining

In our civilized world, breakfast is considered an essential meal of the day. As long as this consisted of—as it did for hundreds of years—fresh cereals or whole-meal porridge mixed with water or milk, warm or cold, or whole-meal bread spread with fresh butter, it most certainly was a good beginning to the day.

However today anyone who eats breakfast consisting of bacon and eggs, cheese and jam, and bread or toast made from extracted white flour goes from one albumin poisoning to the other. It is not surprising that after such a breakfast one feels tired and wants to go back to bed. Proteins produce no immediate energy, and the consumption of too many proteins can cause protein poisoning in the morning. Therefore it is better to start the day with fruit, which contains a lot of water and produces immediate energy and a feeling of fitness. It would therefore be ideal to eat only a light meal in the evening that would then be completely digested during the night. In the morning we can then begin with fruit, and after about twenty minutes, we can eat a tasty whole-meal muesli or whole-meal porridge or whole-grain bread.

People who eat a heavy meal in the evening need a longer period of time for their bodies to detoxify. This means the body should be allowed fourteen to sixteen hours to recover from a heavy meal. Anyone who eats a dinner between 7 and 8 p.m. should then eat a light breakfast (preferably only fruit) around about 10 a.m. to 12 p.m. the next day.

It is a very bad habit, especially after a very large and opulent meal, to serve fruit as a help to the digestion. In this case fruit either helps the digestion immediately by causing diarrhea or starts a fermentation process in the stomach. Imagine the stomach as a barrel; when fruits are added and perhaps also a little alcohol, the digestion process through the entire system could be prolonged up to thirty hours, depending on how heavy the meal was. Normally fruit goes through the stomach within twenty minutes on an empty stomach, but when its way is obstructed by other foods a process of fermentation and decomposition begins. The proteins start to decay, and the content of the stomach becomes acid. We suffer from heartburn, and our breath starts to smell.

Normally digestion in the stomach takes place within four hours when no animal foods have been eaten, but after the consumption of meat, etc., digestion can take eight to ten hours or even more. In both cases, when fruit is eaten at the end of a meal, the period of digestion could be twice as long. However, when we eat the fruit first on an empty stomach, the journey through the stomach to the bowels only takes about twenty minutes. Therefore it is extremely important to eat fruit at least twenty minutes before our mealtime, which allows the fruit to pass through the stomach into the bowels. Apart from being easy to digest, the chewing process while eating fruit has the positive effect of making us feel satisfied earlier than usual.

There is another fundamental rule about food combination that we should follow if we want to eat meat, fish or other animal foods. Our digestive system has not been developed to deal with these foods in combination with carbohydrates, and we should be made aware of the process that takes place when animal proteins are eaten alone or in combination with other kinds of foods. The scientific explanation is extraordinarily complicated and for a layman very difficult to understand. I will therefore try to describe these procedures as simply as possible.

When animal proteins are eaten raw or not mixed with vegetable proteins, they are broken down by stomach acids and can be completely digested and absorbed in the intestines. If meat is heated (grilled, fried, etc.), it should only be heated very quickly, because heat destroys part of the proteins. The longer a piece of meat is heated, the less protein remains. When fried, grilled, roasted or braised meat is eaten together with potatoes, rice, noodles, etc., our body is confronted with an insoluble task. Certain acids are required for the digestion of meat, and others are required to digest alkaline foods. The acids neutralize the alkaline, and the result is that the contents of the stomach start to decompose instead of being digested. The material will stay in the stomach for a prolonged time. The entire process through the digestive system can even take up to thirty hours and in extreme cases up to sixty hours, similar to when we eat fruit after a main meal. This usually results in heartburn, bloating and bad breath.

If one does want to eat meat, then it should only be eaten with salad, uncooked vegetarian foods or quick-heated vegetables that have a high water content. The same goes for cheese, eggs or any other products with animal proteins. Whenever we eat potatoes, rice or noodles or bread, we should not consume any animal proteins, whether in the form of meat, cheese, eggs or fish. Potatoes, rice, noodles or any other starches should only be eaten with vegetables, salad or fruit. It does not matter how well established the habit is of eating meat with potatoes, cheese with bread, etc.; the fact is, it is a bad habit, and here lies one of the keys for a better digestion and a healthier way of life.

We are all creatures of habit, and it is surely difficult for us to reform our way of eating. However, as soon as we have realized that by following this fundamental rule of nature we will begin to feel much better, we will hopefully change.

The Most Important Rules

1. Start the day with fresh fruit that contains a lot of water, such as apples, oranges, pears, grapes, melons, etc. Fruit juices cannot be advised, since essential substances remain behind in the pulp. There is also a tendency to drink too much of one kind when drinking fruit or vegetable juices. Keep in mind, drinking fruit juice or milk is like eating and cannot be considered as a drink.

2. Wait at least twenty to thirty minutes before eating any other food. When eating bananas or similar fruit that has a low water content—this also applies to raw vegetables and salads—the intervals should be prolonged for up to about two hours.

3. To acquire the necessary vitamins and proteins, etc., in the most balanced way, the second meal, twenty minutes after eating fruit, should consist of freshly prepared muesli made out of fresh-ground whole grains. Further details on how to prepare this can be found in the recipes. If you want to eat eggs or meats, they should only be eaten with vegetables or salads.

4. Lunch should consist mainly of salads, vegetables, potatoes, rice or fresh whole-grain noodles (served with sauces and herb dressings or salad oil or fresh butter). If animal foods are to be eaten (fish, meat, eggs or milk products), then one must omit the potatoes, rice or noodles and combine it as proposed.

5. The evening meal should consist of whole-grain bread, whole-grain toast or whole-grain crackers with salad, raw vegetables including tomatoes, onions, garlic, cucumber, etc.

6. Spreads should also be vegetarian. Margarine should be made from cold-pressed oils only, and butter should preferably be cultured from fresh unprocessed milk. If you want to eat animal products such as meat, fish, eggs or cheese, then you must leave out bread and any other products containing starches.

7.   It is permissible to eat fruit before going to bed if this is several hours after the evening meal.

8.   Due to the fact that fruits are refreshing and they give immediate energy, they should always be eaten as a separate meal or on an empty stomach before every meal; after about twenty minutes, the main meal can be eaten.

9.   As it is important that the stomach is empty before eating fruit (otherwise decomposition sets in, as already described), after each meal of fruit, one should wait before eating any grain. Waiting times: After a heavy meal where meat and potatoes, etc., have been eaten, wait eight to ten hours. After a properly combined meal where the above rules have all been kept, wait 4 hours before you serve the next meal. After a pure vegetarian meal, wait three hours. After a salad or raw vegetables, wait two hours.

10.   In the change-over period when the bodily harmony still has not been restored and the impulse to eat something sweet cannot be resisted, then you should only turn to fruits, raw vegetables, fresh nuts, currants or other dried fruits. Due to the fact that carrots, apples, dried fruits and nuts (please, no roasted or salted nuts) need a lot of chewing, the feeling of ravenous hunger usually disappears very quickly.

11.   Rusks, biscuits, cakes and tarts are inferior foods, even when baked with whole-meal flour and sweetened with honey. If you really must eat them, then do so as moderately as possible. Try a homemade cake made of ground spelt or oat and sweetened with a small amount of honey. Layer fresh fruits chopped up small and whole berries with a little whipped cream and chopped nuts. If you do not want to bake yourself, it is possible to buy whole-grain cakes in some health food stores. When experimenting with new recipes it is necessary to follow the basic rules, especially in respect to fruit. This should

preferably not be cooked; fruit is tastier when it is fresh and, of course, much healthier.

12. With a little creativity and flexibility you can conjure up many substitutes or better products to satisfy old but bad habits. For instance, I make my jam out of fresh sweet fruits and berries, chopped or mashed and then spread on whole-meal bread.

Summing up, once again I would like to say that the more natural and unprocessed our food is, the more healthy and digestible it is. If we follow the universal rules and get along without eating animal products, then we need no other complicated rules. If eating meat, remember not to eat carbohydrates with any animal product. If we wish to eat any cooked or processed foods, it is necessary to follow the above rules to the best of our ability so that we can stay healthy and fit.

Chapter Nineteen

Environmental and Agricultural Reform

The Horrible Truth of Mass Breeding

Throughout history human beings have developed many brutal habits. It would be difficult to judge which of these brutalities is the worst, but there is no doubt that today's mass animal breeding and feeding is a nightmare. Anybody who ever has visited a mass producing animal farm will never forget the despair of the confined animals, who have never felt the care or warmth of a mother and have never walked a step in freedom because their cage is constructed in such a way that movement is limited. This reduces the amount of feed necessary and results in higher profits. Some companies are even using animal excrements as feed, utilizing the undigested part of the first bowel movement.

After the animals are fed and raised with the help of a maximum amount of hormones and medication, in the shortest possible time, the ordeal of the transportation begins. They are too weak to stand on their own legs and full of despair and panic; some of them don't survive the trip. To minimize the losses, the animals are drugged.

It is not understandable that the societies for the prevention of cruelty to animals are not acting. When it comes to pets they are very strict and demanding, but the domestic animals are mostly ignored.

All things combined produce a poor quality meat with a high acidity and drug content. When you consider that the industry is advertising the meat as being from happy animals, I wonder where the misleading begins and where it ends.

I am going to skip the killing and the slaughtering. There are several well-researched and detailed books (*Diet of a New America* by Robbins) available on this subject; therefore I prefer to work at constructive proposals of improvement.

Please note that fortunately there are some exceptions where the animals are raised under decent circumstances. But farmers who try to do that can usually only survive if they have found direct customers who honour the better quality with a higher price.

The consumer can demand good and wholesome products. It is therefore not sufficient to impose the normal veterinary controls. Rules must be laid down on how domestic animals are properly kept and how they have to be treated. These must be rules that are internationally agreed upon to avoid any unjust competition. Furthermore, any kind of hormone and other medication that is solely used to increase growth must be strictly forbidden. Since we are consuming the meat and any chemicals in it will end up in our bodies, we must enforce at the same minimum standards for animal medication as we have for human medication.

A Change in Thinking

It is understandable that a company is aiming at maximum profits. However, aside from a legal frame within which companies and farms work, there is also room for morals and ethics.

It is of great importance to ensure that the standards are followed 100 percent. Products today are sold globally. Vital industries in the field of agriculture, food products, drugs, energy and the environment must be guided by international laws and rules into a new direction. In some areas it is possible to make a slow changeover; other areas will need greater speed or even drastic changes.

There has been a gradual change in thinking on the farming industry within the EU commission, which could be another step in a direction that could lead to international agreements. Without these, there is no basis for fair competition. It is time to eliminate all subsidies for farm products and at the same time open up all markets by cutting out customs' duties. Additionally, eliminating pesticides and artificial fertilizers will be the only way to create fair market conditions and to make farming profitable again.

Necessary Reforms

If we want to survive and want to have a life worth living, the foremost change needed is a change of our minds.

Because of the enormity of the task of coping with the ecological, the economical and the health problems of the future, all revolutions and reforms of the past are small compared to what lays ahead.

It does not matter whether we live in the successful western block or in the so-called Third World. It is essential that we find structures, both political and economical, that enable us to have a close relationship and co-operate in the future.

We must urgently solve the most important environmental problems. These include all the individual difficulties in various fields. Examples are: trade and industry, agriculture, food processing, energy, reduction and changeover of all armed forces into an international peace force, drastic reduction of waste and garbage and change of transportation systems. Canada, a country that is perceived around the world as peaceful and united, has a wonderful opportunity to lead this kind of an initiative and join forces with like-minded nations.

All things are connected. There will only be solutions for our challenges if all the problems are tackled together. We have to cut through the vicious circle we have created during the last 200 years of industrialization and the many ongoing wars, including the cold war.

In the beginning of this report I stated that there are simple solutions for all these difficulties. The deeper I delve, the more I am convinced that this is true. The human being has to understand and accept its limitations and the fact that every manipulation of nature or of the laws of nature will bring us backward instead of forward. Without exception, in all areas where we have changed or have disturbed the natural circle we are now experiencing negative result.

These negative examples are manifold and I want to mention a few of them. The continuation of the clearing of the tropical rain forest; the cultivation of monoculture crops; artificial fertilizer; pesticides; mass animal breeding and farming in cramped space are some of the more critical areas. As a result you will find erosion of huge areas throughout the world. Former fertile countries and areas are now depending on a food supply from outside and are fighting for their survival. On the other side, the products are of a decreasing quality in spite of great efforts to create a good appearance with the help of more and more sophisticated methods and the use of more and more chemicals. Initially farmers used these sophisticated methods to get better results, or yields, at lower cost. Today they know that this was one of the great illusions. Many want to turn around, but it takes years to convert land back to natural farming. Only with the help of farming restructuring programs over a longer period are there chances for a cure.

The food processing that has lowered the nutritional value of products considerably has created more so-called denatured products that are only carriers of dead energy, such as refined sugar, white flour and all products made with these ingredients. The same happens with any type of canned meats, fish, vegetables and fruits.

The consumer's behaviour has moved away from simple natural products to more denatured products and to an oversupply of animal protein and fat. This has led to numerous diseases caused by civilization, such as rheumatism, circulatory diseases and disturbances, cancer, weakness of the immune system and allergies.

Drug consumption is one of the worst developments of civilization, compounded by incorrect nourishment and a fierce environment. The development and the usage of atomic arms and atomic energy have changed the world. Increased levels of radiation have changed our lives and implanted mutations into our genes. This brings an incalculable risk to the health and well-being of our future generations.

The excessive burning of our resources of natural oil, gas and other fossil fuels is changing our environment completely. The decreasing ozone layer and the so-called glasshouse effect are a direct threat to our life and any future life on earth.

The revoking of all this will take good will and the willingness to change some of our habits. If we are prepared to do this, we will be able to find ways that don't have to lead us back to the Middle Ages. Quite the opposite is true; there is no limitation for our creativity and our imagination to create new innovation and improve existing systems.

More than anything else we need new products and concepts for our energy management, regardless of whether we are talking about energy for human consumption, oil for our heating systems, gas for our cars or energy for the industry. Once and for all we have to put a taboo on systems and products we cannot control, namely atomic energy.

When this is combined with a change in consumer habits, a drastic reduction of consumption will follow automatically. By changing habits and reducing certain consumptions, we don't have to lower our standard of living. We just have to change it. One first-class example is the new energy-saving light bulb that saves up to 80 percent of energy. Implementing this one little change would save more than 10 percent of our total consumption overnight without lowering our living standard, and the investment would pay for itself within less than three years. Changing designs and insulating our houses and building better homes gives us even greater opportunities for savings. There are numerous other possibilities if we only would be willing to make a few changes for the better. I am convinced that meaningful energy conservation could amount to more than 50 percent savings.

Tremendous savings are possible by changing our packaging systems from single-use plastic containers to returnable systems such as glass or paper. An even better option is to change to even better packaging materials, like flour, which could be converted to compost later on or used as pet food. Furthermore, there are possibilities to sell bulk products in containers owned by the consumer just as in the old days. There are many opportunities for brilliant minds and we could reduce a large portion of all garbage produced.

Consider that more than 70 percent of all areas of agriculture are now utilized for direct or indirect animal or meat production. This is where we have the greatest opportunity for change. This area lends itself for the largest possible reduction of energy and resources used. Even a small reduction has positive effects on life on earth. It must therefore be our most important goal to come to a drastic reduction in the consumption of animal products, including egg and milk products. These products should only be sold in reduced quantities at a level acceptable to our health.

To put this into practice covering all the mentioned areas sounds like a gigantic and impossible task. This is not so; only one little change is necessary, and this change has to take place in our mind. If we succeed in changing our mind, the rest will follow relatively easily. It took human beings thousands of years to accept the fact that the earth is round. Let us hope that it will take less time to understand that we have to conserve and use our energy and resources in a different way in the future. The "energy revolution" must start right now. It is our only chance for turning things around!

Ways of Implementing the Reforms

It is the goal of this report to give the leaders of this world ideas and thoughts. It will be most important to find an international platform through which all the reforms can be implemented. This should be part of the United Nations. On the other hand, it needs to be a separate, efficient, small but strong unit that will not be drowned in the bureaucracy of a United Nations main organization. Just like the creation of the agency for Innovation and Job Creation I talk about in the first part of this book, we need to find a governance structure that can inspire and enforce change with a clear mandate.

Each nation should only send one representative, preferably a person with direct contact to the leader of her or his country. This person should have the mandate to vote on behalf of the respective nation. All decisions must be carried by a majority, and the size of the voting right will be calculated on the basis of population, size of the country and the gross national product. If you limit the amount of delegates from each country to one or two people and initially accept the membership of the forty leading countries the total number of people could be less than 100. An institute or agency of this size with proper authorization could be as effective as "dynamite." This institute could, in a reasonably short time, work out the frame and the time schedule for the various reforms.

The direct cost of this "Institute for Reforms and Conversion" could initially be limited to a few hundred thousand dollars per nation. The management of the institute should consist of a handful of top professionals under the guidance of a strong and dedicated leader who should be a well-respected person internationally. This management team could coordinate all the activities and implement the reforms via the United Nations and the International Peace force, and any other suitable and feasible ways of execution to be determined by the members. It should have access to the pertinent data banks of all the member countries.

It could reside at the head office of the UN or anywhere in the world, but preferably at a neutral place like Sweden or Switzerland. It might also be advisable to place it in an eastern/far eastern location like St. Petersburg, Berlin, Singapore or Hong Kong.

There is no reason why this Institute could not start in the near future. Initially it should lay down its own working rules to enable an effective way of co-operation, then establish a list of priorities and divide the members into small working groups that can take over certain tasks. For each task there must be a definite timeframe set, of which all member countries will be informed.

Projects of Priority

International demilitarization, converting the national armies into an international peace force that will work under the UN, will be one of the key priorities, to destroy all atomic arms and to dismantle all other conventional and non-conventional weapons and systems except for a sufficient armament for a peace force.

Make a world food plan based on the natural production potential of each country. Based on the production, cost feasibility studies could be done to establish where the most efficient farming takes place for which product mix.

Eliminating any unnecessary trucking or shipping will be another great opportunity to save resources. Prices need to be established allowing sufficient margins for profits and investments. A quota system for each product can be worked out for each area, promoting all natural products and defining a surcharge for each denatured product and all animal products.

Forbidding all pesticides and artificial fertilizers not essential for effective natural farming.

Planning a drastic reduction of any form of pollution is another key area. This includes energy production, transportation equipment and eliminating unnecessary packaging and chemicals.

A gradual changeover from atomic energy to alternative power systems such as wind, solar, tidal, biomass and hydrogen, etc., must begin.

Likewise the medical and pharmaceutical professions, along with their manufacturing counterparts, will need to be restructured. A focus on prevention will help to reduce drug consumption. The number of approved drugs and chemicals must be reduced. It will be difficult but rewarding to convert to natural methods of healing and natural herbs and medication. The internationally organized public treatment of all drug addicts will make this whole area more transparent. Any kind of production of and/or dealing in illegal drugs must be made impossible and further punished with a very strong penalty. The drug farmers must be given an opportunity to convert to other farming or be given an altogether different occupation.

All the combined measurements will reduce the amount of garbage to a small part of the present level. The remaining garbage has to be handled in a way that separates the various kinds of materials for recycling. Each household has to do the pre-selection and is responsible for the proper handling of this.

The change of our climate is one of our main concerns. It is therefore necessary to develop an exact time frame for the different steps. We can under no circumstances allow the continuation of our present level of pollution. It is therefore not enough to bring the pollution to a halt; we need a drastic reduction followed by a step-by-step elimination of the main pollution sources.

This report and plan, which is meant to be an inspiration to get active today in all fields mentioned, will possibly be considered utopian. But tomorrow this kind of plan may be a necessity for mankind to survive!

When the UN was founded there were plenty of critics. However, in spite of its struggles, the UN plays an important role in many areas today. The time is probably right to review its mandate and to move ahead into the next phase. Again, we must expect the critics and "preventers" of change to oppose this. That is no reason to be discouraged. Visions and dreams are always the beginning of any major change or shift. In the long-term, they will prevail!

Canada as a respected nation could easily initiate a change at the UN. It will solely depend upon the political will, passion and leadership. The timing for change is right.

We cannot continue on the present path. Even in the U.S. there are more and more voices who demand the U.S. leave the path of policing and bullying the rest of the world. Annual military spending in the U.S. has reached almost $500 billion or 50 percent of the world's $1 trillion a year (www.globalissues.org/geopoli tics/armstrade/spending). It is time to turn this around and use some of these gigantic sums for something more productive. Only a concerted effort under a UN mandate will in the long run succeed to unite the world around common practical goals.

Chapter Twenty

Guidance for the Changeover to High Quality Wholesome Food

I have already pointed out how important fresh whole grains are for your diet. It should be served as muesli in the form of freshly milled grain from your own little stone mill. Any type of fresh whole grain, preferably oat, spelt, wheat or rye, will play a very important role in your future natural kitchen. You can buy the grain directly from a farmer for about $0.15 per pound or from a health food store for $0.50 per pound. The famous saying that an Asian can live on a handful of rice holds true for other grains. We can almost solely live on 250 grams of fresh grain, such as wheat, at the cost of 7.5 to 25 cents per day.

A good example of this occurred in Denmark during and after World War I. When most of Europe was starving, the Danish government imposed a reduction of meat and milk production in favour of the much cheaper grain and vegetable production. This way Denmark was the only country in Europe where people received enough wholesome and healthy food throughout the entire war. As a side effect of this much more healthy diet, the health level of the entire population improved.

If we had the same progressive thinking today there, would be no supply problems whatsoever. But unfortunately people still have many misconceptions about the importance of animal products.

Please memorize the earlier mentioned ground rules for the preparation and the intake of your food. These are extremely important for your digestion and well-being, particularly when a non-vegetarian eats mixed foods.

Here is some other vital information that might surprise you: the average North American or European consumes approximately two to three thousand calories of mixed food per day (according to the Food and Agriculture Organisation of the UN, the food consumed is mainly animal based). With this kind of animal-based nutrition, roughly 60 percent of total energy is used for digestion; if the ground rules are not obeyed, it could even be more. If food is eaten in the proper order, this level can be reduced by 10 to 20 percent down to 40 to 50 percent energy use. The higher the percentage of animal-based products, the higher the input of energy required for digestion. Overweight people can use up to 80–90 percent of their total available energy for digestion of food. Some people believe that by using so much energy for digestion they avoid gaining weight. This is a complete misunderstanding. When you use 90 percent of all available energy for digestion alone, you have barely 10 percent left for all other activities. This can amount to a great passivity compared to normal people. On the other hand, a vegetarian who obeys the ground rules needs a maximum of 20 to 30 percent of his energy for digestion. I can confirm this sensational finding. After changing my eating habits, my need for sleep has been reduced by almost two hours nightly from eight to six hours, and yet I feel stronger and more energetic than before. This indicates the possible performance of the mixed-food eater is much smaller than the possible performance of the vegetarian eater, a difference of up to 50–60 percent! Even if I have never found any western research data available that confirms what Asian monks throughout the years have told me, I do not for a minute doubt these conclusions. I have throughout the roughly 30 years of being a vegetarian again and again seen the bid difference first hand and experienced it for myself.

Some Whole Food Recipes and How to Convert and Develop New Recipes

Why Soaking is so Important

When we are using grains, nuts, almonds, raisons, legumes, etc. we need to remember that these products in the drying process have lost a substantial amount of their natural water content. If we want to mill the grain, it is important for the grain to be as dry as possible, and the same applies for any other products we want to mill. However in preparing the muesli ingredients, we do not like to cut or grind the almonds, nuts and even raisins before soaking. They should preferably be soaked for twenty-four hours, and then you can chop them with a knife.

The soaking has various effects: the products will taste fresh, and they will be digested more easily. The enzyme creation will also be improved by soaking; therefore it will be advantageous to soak for some time.

When we are dealing with flaxseed or any other tiny seeds, it will be easiest to first grind and then soak. The penetration in small seeds is faster and easier; therefore these can be ground or milled, for example, right after milling the oat grain and soaked together with the grain when you prepare your muesli. (Remember to use a small coffee grinder for the flax seed.)

When you are preparing legumes for your dinner, it is usually ideal to let them soak for twenty-four to (maximum) forty-eight hours.

Natural Raw Muesli (for two people)

60 g (2 oz) oats (can be replaced by any grain except rice)
100 g (3.4 oz) water
1 teaspoon of freshly squeezed lemon juice
15–25 raisins, some dried prunes
15 almonds and/or 1–2 walnuts freshly chopped (soaked in fresh water for 24 hours)
20 g of ground flaxseed can be added (use small coffee grinder to mill oily seeds and nuts). Flaxseed is very valuable and helps your digestion.

Mill the raw oat grain in a stone mill. Then mix the oat flour with dried fruits and nuts and add lemon juice and water. Let soak before eating (minimum 30–40 minutes and maximum 8 hours).

Depending on your appetite you can mix as many cut fresh fruit of any kind with the soaked coarse flour. If you are certain (confirmed by blood tests by your doctor) that you don't have a milk allergy, then you may add a small amount of milk or yogourt. But you have to be certain about this; many people have a milk allergy without knowing it and wonder why they have digestive system complaints. Soya milk is an excellent alternative and is readily available.

Daily muesli is your foundation for a good and healthy life. It will supply you with most of the vital products your body needs, including vitamins A, C, E and B complex, energy and important minerals. This very light and yet hearty meal gives you a wonderful start to the day.

Anyone who has difficulties getting up in the morning can mill and soak the grain at night just before going to bed. However you have to make sure to prevent oxidation by covering the fresh flour completely with water and a tablespoon of lemon juice. The raisins, the fresh cut fruit and the nuts are then added in the morning. Never let it soak more than eight to nine hours. Thereafter the loss of vitamins is drastic.

The amount of work for the muesli is easily tackled if the whole family participates. Milling take one to two minutes; then soak the grain before you go to the bathroom. Later when the family is assembled in the kitchen, it takes a few minutes of joint effort to cut the fruit and prepare the rest.

Before I changed to muesli and whole food in the morning, I would soon feel tired and exhausted after a heavy meal of eggs and meats. Even though the muesli is a more complete and nourishing meal, it is much lighter. You will also feel this and be surprised by the difference. Furthermore you will find that this meal will get you through the day much better even if you skip your lunch once in a while. Your body's urge for vital products is now reduced because your meals are properly balanced. You will find that your former craving and hunger feelings for sweets will more or less disappear within a few weeks. If the cravings should return, you should satisfy them with some fresh fruit, some carrots or a nice salad. It is almost always possible to eat an apple. There is a lot of merit in the saying "one apple a day keeps the doctor away"!

In Between Meals

Along with the ground rules I listed previously the waiting periods recommended between consuming different types of food. Particularly when you want to eat fruit you have to follow these instructions strictly.

After your morning muesli and after a break of at least two hours, you can eat as much fruit as you wish if you feel hungry again. Remember to always start with the fruit with the highest water content; these are digested fastest. Bananas should be eaten last as they contains starch and take much longer to digest.

You can always replace a main meal with fruit, raw vegetables, salad, nuts and dried fruit. Your fitness improves when you do this regularly. Again you should follow the sequence of fruit, vegetables and salad first, nuts and dried fruit last.

As long as you follow the waiting period, you can eat muesli any time of the day. If you don't have enough time for thirty minutes of soaking, you can replace the raw wheat or spelt with raw oat grain/oats. When you mill medium-fine or fine oatmeal, it only requires five to ten minutes of soaking. You can also buy processed oat flakes, but remember that due to oxidation after being processed, they have lost most of their vitamins—although I would still prefer the oat flakes compared to most other commercial cereals.

Mixed dried fruit and raw nuts are also a wonderfully wholesome meal in between and satisfy people who still have a sweet tooth. But don't buy these mixed. Select only first-class freshly dried products and avoid any salted, roasted or heated nuts. Avoid any sulphur-treated or otherwise chemically treated products.

You can use dried fruit and various nuts for many things. You should therefore always keep a good selection available. Avoid any type of roasted peanuts; these should also be eaten raw or steamed but many people don't like them this way. Particularly at the beginning, you may still have a strong craving for sweet products. To prevent a fall back to chocolates, candies or other sugar products, you should always have an ample supply of fresh fruit and dried fruits around you.

I want to mention that chocolates contain stimulants, which are very attractive to a lot of people. I am one of these people. I found that small quantities of bitter chocolate consumed on special occasions cannot do great harm. It is important to read the label and make sure it contains approximately 70 percent chocolate, maximum 30 percent of sugar and preferably no milk or milk products. But don't fool yourself; the emphasis must be on moderation!

After a few weeks your interest for sweets will diminish. Your body will feel very well with all the fresh, wholesome products. The intestinal flora improves dramatically, although older or recovering people sometimes should add good quality intestinal bacteria like acidophilus and bifidus. Digestion has improved, and you will find that bowel movements are softer and regular, once or twice a day. However you will get complications as soon as you eat any sugar or white flour products. The flora is no longer geared for these denatured products, and you can get flatulence that can be quite painful. You should therefore avoid any products that could contain sugar, white flour or similar denatured raw materials, such as heated fruit products or heated honey. Initially this seems to be very difficult, but after a while you will develop a routine and automatically detect these and stay clear of them.

In some people a drastic change in diet can involve complications. Many years of unhealthy eating and living habits have possibly created a chronic illness or a state in which your system needs additional help. Try to use live cultures like acidophilus, bifidus, l.casei or l.reuteri. You can get these in good quality yogourts or in pill form. When you eat yogourt, remember that the yogourt is much easier to digest if it doesn't contain any fruit.

Dinner

I trust that you have studied the chapter about the necessary tools to prepare your meals and that you have bought these. It is also easier to have a certain stock of supplies on hand. This allows you to focus primarily on fresh produce on a daily basis and saves a lot of time.

In every country, food traditions and habits differ. When I talk about dinner, I mean the meal at noon, which is usually a warm meal in Northern Europe. When I talk about the meal in the evening, I mean *Abendbrot*, which translates into *evening bread* with the main emphasis on *bread*. You will no doubt develop your own habits. The important thing is to follow the laws of nature rather than any artificial rules. In my own household where two very different cultures (Chinese and North European) came together, you can well imagine that at the beginning we had some differences of opinion when it came to food.

Due to the climate and lack of refrigeration in China, all three main meals of the day are heated. For health reasons this was always a necessity, and most likely this can never change in a country like China. But the Chinese have mastered this by developing the wok. The raw materials are bought fresh daily at the market. The chopping takes some effort, while the heating will only take a few minutes and cause a minimum loss of vitamins. Vegetables even maintain their colour, and the loss of value is minimal as long as you master the technique and use first-class oils and raw materials.

I am mentioning all this to encourage you to make the change regardless of your location. Most areas have their own good traditions and products, and you will find this natural way of preparing your food can be adjusted easily. You will also find that before industrialization and before denatured products were developed, most cultures followed similar natural rules. You must therefore obey the laws of nature regardless of where you are or what raw materials you want to use and the traditional habits of the region. Follow the rules I carefully explained to you, and try to eat at least 60 percent of your food raw or fresh. Eat only fresh and live foods, no dead processed products, and as much as possible keep away from any animal products, including those made from milk or eggs. Remember that we all have an oversupply of protein and that vegetables, fruit, nuts and grain give us all the nutrients and energy (including protein) we need and more. All the whole-grain products and most vegetables have more than 10 percent of various proteins; we need only around 2 percent. Remember that proteins can only be utilized fully in our bodies if they have not been heated over 42° C (approximately 103° F). The proteins we eat are converted into amino acids and then in our digestive system back to proteins.

Preparation of Salads

Wholesome also means fresh. When you buy the salad and the vegetables, select every item with great care. Don't look only at the beauty; instead, examine them for quality. For example, cucumbers or tomatoes from hothouses usually look much better than the outdoor variety, but the quality is usually lower. Don't hesitate to look for the origin or to ask the store manager where he gets his products, how old these are, when they are delivered and how often per week they get new supplies. The more they can see your interest, the more they will be motivated to get you good selections of quality products.

Salad—Salad—Salad

Never forget to serve salad before each meal. Apart from the fact that a nicely prepared salad is a real delicacy, it has several functions. The fact is that your craving for food is more or less satisfied after twenty minutes of chewing. If you need ten to fifteen minutes of chewing for your salad, you will never eat too much of the dishes that follow. But if you start with fat, starches, meat and other heavy foods, you may eat several times the amount of calories you need. Furthermore you should follow the rule of proper order. First eat the fruit, salads and vegetables, then the starches or alternative moderate amounts of animal products. This way your digestion will require the smallest amount of energy.

A few important facts or rules that will make it easy to convert your favourite salad dishes into more healthy variations are as follows:

You can use most vegetables or fruits for your salad. The only exceptions are certain types of beans and a few other exotic products that have to be cooked because otherwise they are poisonous or indigestible. Furthermore, you can use many types of nuts and dried fruit to create variations. Use your imagination and preferably prepare food shortly before eating it, and you will always have success with your salads.

Remember that nuts can be difficult to digest. It helps if they are soaked in water for twenty-four hours. In our household we therefore always have a few small bowls with soaking nuts.

If possible, do not use any premixed dressings. You want to select and make sure of using only fresh ingredients. Most important is your choice of cold pressed oil. A natural oil is not fattening and is very important for your metabolism.

Some facts about cold pressed oils:

Olive oil is pressed at 43° Celsius. It is an ideal all-around oil for salads, baking and cooking.

Sunflower seed oil is pressed at around 46° Celsius. It is rich in linol acids and also good for all-around usage.

Thistle oil is pressed at slightly higher temperatures (around 60° Celsius). But if the process is careful and gentle, it is still considered a cold press. This oil is very light and an all-around oil but mainly for salads.

Sesame oil is pressed at lower temperatures (42° Celsius); of the mentioned oils this one is ideal for cooking and baking at high temperatures and also ideal for all-around usage.

There are many more other popular oils that all are of good quality as long as the raw material is good (preferably naturally farmed) and they are pressed at low temperatures.

Natural fruit vinegar from the store, or even better homemade, is ideal for making salad dressings. To make this you press fresh apples and leave the juice in open bottles in your cool basement. After the fermentation, I usually cover the bottles with a small piece of clean cloth and fasten it with a small rubber band. This way the vinegar is well protected and yet can breathe. Such vinegar is ideal to mix with any type of chopped herbs, garlic, cucumbers, olives, peppers and onions, etc. If this is too much work, you can take any natural fruit vinegar and then do your own chopping and mixing of the various ingredients. Make a sure that your choice of natural vinegar isn't pasteurized.

Yogourt, Kefir, Cream, Cottage Cheese, Other Milk Products and Eggs

As long as these are natural wholesome products, you can use them in your dressings and sauces in many ways. Please remember that they also are animal products and not everybody is able to eat or digest them. In any event, I recommend using only small quantities.

Salt

Salt should always be the so-called sea salt, which apart from sodium also contains a lot of other salts and minerals. However even sea salt is basically not organic and not easily digested. Therefore many years ago I stopped using commercial sea salt or salt altogether and only use "BRAGGS." This is a seasoning using the natural salt of the soya bean. You can buy it in most health food stores. This product is one of many products developed by the legendary Dr. Bragg. He has written fascinating books about water, salt, apple cider vinegar and fasting.

Herbs and Spices

Use only fresh herbs in season. The spices should be freshly ground in your own pepper mill. If fresh herbs are not obtainable, you can use fresh-frozen products.

Top Fit Salad

It is always a great pleasure to prepare a nice fresh salad. I rely on the seasonal products that are plentiful in supply, good in quality and usually very reasonable in price. As the green lettuce I always take the one that is freshest: normal green lettuce, iceberg lettuce, field lettuce, spinach, chicory, endives, etc. Then I take tomatoes, radishes, green, red and yellow peppers and cut these into pieces or slices, and then I chop some carrots and parsley and mix everything together with the greens.

To this I add a simple but very delicious sauce. The sauce is made of 1 normal-sized chopped onion, 1 middle-sized chopped or crushed clove of garlic, 3 tablespoons of fresh squeezed lemon juice, 2 tablespoons of olive oil, 1 teaspoon of sesame oil, 1 teaspoon of liquid honey, 1 tablespoon of BRAGGS and plenty of fresh ground black pepper. I mix everything thoroughly with 1 teaspoon of tomato paste.

Red Beet Salad

One of the healthiest vegetables available is the red beet. When you grate it or shred it into tiny little pieces you can eat it raw.

Use 1 red beet and shred it together with 1 apple or pear. Add 2 tablespoons of fresh lemon juice; mix and serve it on a bed of lettuce. Chop some hazelnuts or walnuts and put them on top.

Radish–Tomato–Cucumber Salad

A small bundle of radishes is cut into slices and covered with chives, then a sauce of yogourt, thistle oil and fruit vinegar is poured over it. Tomatoes are sliced and covered with chopped parsley and onions; the sauce is made of lemon, olive oil, 1 tablespoon BRAGGS and 1/2 teaspoon of honey. Cucumbers are cut into slices and covered with chopped dill, BRAGGS, fresh ground pepper and sesame oil. All three salads are served in three piles on a lettuce bed on one plate. This makes a very refreshing and decorative serving of salad.

Salad of Carrots

200g (7oz) of rasped carrots, 3 tablespoons lemon juice, 2 tablespoons sun seed oil, 5 chopped walnuts, fresh ground pepper, parsley and lettuce. Everything is mixed properly and served on a bed of lettuce.

Radish or Celery Root Salad

200g (7oz) of shredded radish or celery root, 2 tablespoons fruit vinegar, 2 tablespoons thistle oil, 1 shredded apple and mandarins for decoration. Use fresh ground pepper, spices or herbs as desired.

Red Cabbage Salad

200g (7oz) of sliced red cabbage, 1 large onion, 2 tablespoons of thistle oil, 1 tablespoon of fruit vinegar, 1 tablespoon of lemon juice. The onion is chopped into small pieces and mixed well with cabbage and the dressing.

This and similar salads can be made from many different vegetables. Some of these are: cauliflower, brussel sprouts, peppers, fennel, broccoli, field lettuce and spinach. To all these salads you can add as many raw mushrooms, various herbs, BRAGGS and spices as you like.

All salads are prepared without refined sugar. If you want a certain sweetness you can add shredded fruit, like apples, pears or pineapples; small amounts of honey or maple syrup are also acceptable.

In order to get as large a selection as possible with the highest possible content of vitamins and minerals, you should work your sprout-producing unit continuously. This way you can add 1 to 2 oz. of germinated grains or seeds. Your own germination guarantees a constant fresh supply and a drastic increase in natural vitamins and other vital elements. Sprouting or germinating will take some training and knowledge. If done incorrectly, fungus will grow in it; therefore I propose that you buy a book on sprouting. It will help you to get first-class results. You can sprout any kind of live nut, almond, legume, grain, etc. All the organic products are usually live, and most of them already part of your stocked raw materials.

Furthermore, you can add various tofu products (made from soya) and a variety of eggs and cheeses both for decoration and for taste. The sauces can be varied by adding sweet or sour cream, yogourt, kefir and similar milk- or soya-based materials. Also, whole-grain noodles are an excellent variation but not in combination with animal or soya products. I use only homemade whole-grain noodles or fresh whole-grain noodles from the store.

As always you should try to follow the rules. The less animal products you use, the lighter and more digestible the salads will be.

All the raw categories of your future diet—grains, seeds, fruits, nuts and vegetables—should represent roughly 60 percent of your total food intake. The remaining 40 percent will then be a mixture of many products, such as breads, potatoes, rice and many other prepared products. As we continue, we will deal will all these items, including soups and desserts.

As soon as your mind has changed and you get used to the freshness of your delicate meals, you will love it as much or more than your former kitchen.

Soups

It is not my intention to make this into a cooking book. However it is important to give you an idea of how whole food nutrition works and a few basic recipes to enable you to convert your present favourite dishes. It will help you to develop your own techniques for future cooking.

The broth for the soup should always be vegetable based. A meat-based broth does not really taste any better and it is strongly acid forming in your body.

You can buy vegetable-based broth concentration in most health food stores and even some grocery stores. But much better is your homemade broth that you can easily make yourself.

Natural Vegetable Broth

1 litre (a little over 1 quart) of water, 1 kg of any kind of chopped vegetables of the season, including some carrots, some radish roots, parsley and similar herbs; 3–4 small onions, several cloves of garlic, 2 bay leafs, 1 clove, some freshly ground nutmeg and pepper, some BRAGGS and some pimento.

Let the broth boil for 5 minutes and leave it on a low flame for 25 minutes. You can eat this as a vegetable soup, even leaving the ingredients and adding some fresh vegetables in the last five minutes on the low heat, such as peas, spinach, cauliflower, cucumber, radish etc. You can also put the base soup through a sieve and use it as a clear soup or for other meals. You can furthermore make an excellent salted (BRAGGS) vegetable base that will keep in a glass jar in your fridge for several days or weeks depending upon the amount of BRAGGS and spices used.

Salted (BRAGGS) Vegetable Base

Take the same or similar vegetables as for the above broth, possibly including some green leek. Chop it up into small tiny pieces by hand or with your kitchen machine and fry it very briefly in vegetable oil. After this, mix it carefully with 8 tablespoons of BRAGGS and some pepper. Pour it into a glass jar and store it in your fridge; whenever you want to make some soup base, use 1-2 tablespoons per litre (1 quart).

You can now venture out and prepare any kind of soup. Avoid overcooking the main ingredients; in most cases a few minutes of heating of the vegetables in the broth is sufficient. I will give you a few examples of some nice soups.

Mushroom Soup

Take 200g (approx 1/2 lb) mushrooms; cut these into slices and fry them together with 2–3 chopped onions and 2 tomatoes. Take 1 litre of your vegetable broth; heat this very briefly together with your mushrooms and onions. Put a little chopped parsley or leek on top. You can, of course, also use dried mushrooms if you soak them sufficiently.

Tomato Soup

Take 1 kg (approx 2 lbs) of fresh tomatoes and 3 chopped onions and fry them in some oil or butter together with a few diced garlic cloves. You grind the fresh tomatoes in your mixer and put it together with 1 litre of boiling vegetable broth. You round it off with some pepper, paprika and spices. For decoration and taste you can put some whipped cream and chopped chives on top.

Leek Soup

Take 500 g (1 lb) of sliced leek and fry them for a short time in vegetable oil. Whip 2 egg yolks and 1/2 of a pint of cream. Mix it in 1 litre of vegetable broth and round it off with spices and pepper. You can also put a little bit of grated cheese on top and/or some parsley.

Green Pea Soup with Oat Balls

To prepare the oat balls you grind 250g of oats (approx 1/2 lb); mix it with 1/2 litre (1/2 quart) of water and 2 tablespoons of concentrated vegetable soup. Boil this for 1 minute and leave it on the turned-off burner for 15 minutes. After the mixture has cooled for at least 1 hour, mix this with 3 eggs, 1 tablespoon of mustard, some spices, celery powder and BRAGGS. Form small balls that are then fried and ready for your soup. The soup is made out of 1 litre of broth and 1/2 lb of fresh or frozen peas which you boil for 1 minute. Serve as many oat balls with the soup as you like; the rest of the oat balls are ideal for meals the next day.

Guidelines and Recommendations for Main Dishes

You can again use most of your favourite dishes, but remember if you want to eat any animal products in your main dish you should serve only vegetables or salads and no starches. If you want to eat potatoes, rice or noodles, eat these together with vegetables or salads only. If you want to have a replacement for the meat products whenever you eat starches, you can of course use any kind of tofu, make nice grain balls, veggie burgers and mushroom casseroles. The only type of meat you can eat together with the starch products are raw, dried or cold smoked items. Some of these are smoked or raw ham, beef, lamb and fish. I do not recommend this, but if you absolutely want it this is the only way you should eat meat products together with starches.

Whenever you cook meat or fish dishes you will come into a situation of conflict. On one side you must know that overcooking means killing most of the vitamins and even the main ingredient, the protein, while not cooking enough can mean a bad infection such as hepatitis, salmonella poisoning, etc. It is therefore very important that you can trust your butcher and that he trusts his suppliers. Given the severity of the consequences, I strongly advise you to make sure to heat the products sufficiently. When you do this you will know that because of the heating there is very little value left in it.

There are therefore two important reasons to drastically reduce or to skip animal products completely:

1. If you want to improve your chances for good health!

2. To ensure that you and your children will live in an environment worth living in.

A few examples of main dishes will again enable you to adjust to this new way of thinking. When you have taken the first steps in this direction, you should buy additional cookbooks that can guide you. In all European countries, in Canada and in U.S., you will find a good selection in most health food and bookstores. And when you strictly apply the few important rules you have learned, you can overcome most shortcomings there may be.

Remember for all your future cooking never again to use any denatured products. When we are talking flour, we mean only fresh-ground whole-grain flour, fresh-made whole-grain noodles or natural rice. Potatoes are only boiled for ten to fifteen minutes, always in their skins. To peel a potato before cooking means to throw away most of the good stuff. Never overcook any of your vegetables, even if you are used to the overcooked taste and consider this taste delicious. After a few days you will acquire a taste for the new way.

Once you have learned the basic rules of nature, of natural cooking and the relation between energy and food, your outlook on life will change. I am sure that your pride in dealing with all these things and the valuable knowledge you have obtained will eventually make you relieved and happy.

Carrots, Leek and Oat Balls

You take 1 pound of leek and 1 pound of carrots. After cutting them into thin slices you fry them very quickly under high heat in a little butter and round it off with additional butter and parsley. You fry your oat balls separately in oil using the same recipe as before (green pea soup and oat balls). You can serve this together with nice baked potatoes. For variety you can also put some slices of cheese on top of the carrots and bake it for 10 minutes in your oven.

Eggplant and Rice

Take one nice size eggplant, cut it into small cubes and fry it in oil together with some onions and garlic. Add some soya milk and a little BRAGGS. You can serve this together with potatoes, rice or noodles.

Noodle Casserole

Take 1 lb of fresh whole-grain noodles. Cut 2 onions and some chives into small dices and fry these in oil for 1 minute only. Add 100 g of sliced mushrooms. Mix everything together with the noodles, adding spices and BRAGGS. Put everything into a glass casserole. Scramble 2 eggs together with 2 tablespoons of cream and some spices and BRAGGS. Put this on top and bake it for 20 minutes in your oven. Even better than the scrambled eggs would be some chopped or sliced tofu.

Cauliflower and Home-Fried Raw Potatoes

Steam one middle-sized cauliflower. Cut 2 lbs properly cleaned potatoes into slices (skin on); fry them together with 2 onions (rings). Heat 2 tomato halves, for 1 minute. Before serving, put some fresh ground nutmeg on the cauliflower and BRAGGS, pepper and chopped parsley on the potatoes.

Green Beans and Mushrooms

Take 1 lb of green beans; steam them for 15 minutes. The last five minutes you add 200g of sliced mushrooms. Put some butter and chopped chives or other herbs in season on top and serve it with potatoes, rice or noodles.

Spinach Soup with Peeled Potatoes

Take 1/2 litre (1 quart) of vegetable broth and boil 1 lb of spinach; dice 2 onions and add to spinach. Serve this together with peeled potatoes and one soft-boiled egg per person.

Celery-Steak and Mixed Vegetables and Sprouts

Boil 1 celery root or 1 big radish (approximately 1 lb) in 1 litre of vegetable broth for 20 minutes . Take it out and cut it into whole slices of 1 cm (1/2 inch). Turn the slices in egg and then whole-grain breadcrumbs. Fry the slices in oil, and serve the steaks together with some raw vegetables and mixed sprout vegetables. Use the broth and make a nice sauce out of it. Use whole-grain fine flour to thicken it and add finely chopped parsley.

Bread

In some countries bread together with a spread or filling is a main dish. In my home country we sometimes eat bread after the oats in the morning and almost always bread at night served with all kinds of spreads, vegetables, fruit, sausages, smoked meat and fish, and last but not least, with a variety of many cheeses.

Even if I recommend muesli in the morning for everybody regardless of culture or background, I don't mind once in a while enjoying a slice of fresh-baked bread with a little honey or fresh-made jam (mashed fresh fruit). As a matter of fact, whenever my wife and I are ready for a special treat, we eat a little of our traditional dishes after our muesli. I have bread, and she has a rice dish.

But whenever you do this, do not forget the rules. Eat your fruit and your muesli first and then a slice of bread, the rice or the noodles.

If you want to put sausage or meat products on the bread, you are only allowed to use raw, dried or cold smoked items. If you use cheeses, keep in mind they are affecting your health the same way as any other animal products; use them sparingly. A piece of bread can be just as nice with cucumber, tomatoes, radishes, salads or just some churned butter. You can furthermore buy many delicious vegetarian spreads or make them yourself to be sure that the proper ingredients are used. Buy margarines that are made of cold-pressed oils. Standard margarine that is made from processed oils is a direct threat to your health. Buy only fresh grade-1 churned/cultured butter, no mixtures.

When you buy bread make absolutely sure that the bread is made of whole grain. You have to find out which baker in your neighbourhood bakes proper whole-grain bread. Most supermarkets carry a variety of whole wheat, rye, oat or blended breads. When you buy the bread, look at the label. Good quality traditional sour dough or yeast whole-grain bread will only consist of whole-grain flour, water, yeast/sour dough and a minimal quantity of salt. Some of the sliced whole-grain toast is produced with a lot of protein, chemicals, preservatives and antioxidants. I try to stay away from these and go with my own or the traditional breads.

Under any circumstances I strongly recommend that you bake your own bread if you are not sure of the supply. Buy a good baking book with whole-grain recipes. To get you started I will give you some of my easier recipes.

Standard Wheat or, Even Better, Spelt Bread

500 g (1.1 lbs) fine fresh-ground whole spelt/wheat flour
1/8 litre of water
1/8 litre of soya milk (if not available, water or buttermilk)
10 g of dry yeast (2 teaspoons) or sour dough
3 oz of ground flaxseed
1 tablespoon honey
1 tablespoon BRAGGS

Put into an automated breadmaker. Or do it the traditional way by hand: Put the flour into a dish, dig a small hole in the middle and put the yeast in crumbs or powder into it. Add 3 tablespoons of lukewarm soya milk and knead this and part of the flour into a dough. Cover it with a cloth and leave this for half an hour at a warm spot (oven at 50° Celsius).

After this you add the remaining ingredients and knead this for 10 minutes into a dough. You can do this by hand or with a dough-kneading machine (part of any better-made kitchen machine).

Now you form the bread loaf. Put some fat on the baking tin before putting the bread on it. Let the bread rise for another hour and bake it for 45 minutes at 200° Celsius. When the bread is still warm, you put some butter on the surface.

Rye Bread

For pure rye bread you can use the same recipe as for wheat/spelt. You will get a mixed bread by dividing into 250 g whole spelt flour and 250 g whole rye flour and add 200g of sunflower seeds, which are mixed in without grinding.

Muffins out of Barley and Oats

1 lb of mixed whole flour of barley and oats (50/50)
4 teaspoons of baking powder or yeast
1 tablespoon of BRAGGS
1 teaspoon of vanilla
2 tablespoons of honey
1 quart of soya milk or buttermilk
5 tablespoons of sesame oil
4 oz. of ground linseed

You mix first the dry and the liquid materials separately and then together. If you have muffin papers you put the dough into these; otherwise you form small balls, each 2 oz, and put them on the oiled baking tin. There are hundreds of wonderful recipes from Ireland, England, France, Germany, Denmark, Russia, from all the Mediterranean countries, U.S.A., Canada, Mexico, etc. They are all good as long as they are whole grain. Select your own favourites and develop your own recipes with and without raisins, ground linseed and nuts.

Cakes

Traditional cakes are like gunpowder to our health. Having a weakness for cakes, I have found my own sneaky way to enjoy a regular piece of cake without sinning too much. Again we should follow our rules in respect to only using whole-grain flours, honey instead of sugar and as many raw products as possible. Furthermore, we have to consider the waiting periods between meals.

We can adapt most cake recipes according to these rules and come up with very tasty products, but I want to give you four recipes that are a little different. This will help you to start your own creative development in other directions.

Short Pastry Cake

500 g wheat flour (1.1 lbs), 4 teaspoons baking powder, 2 eggs, 2 tablespoons of honey, 200 g (7oz) of butter, vanilla, rasped lemon skin and 2 tablespoons of rum. You have to knead this carefully and leave it for 30 minutes. Then you roll in onto 2 flat round oiled springform pans or 1 oven plate and bake it in the oven for 25 minutes.

You can now cover the cakes with 2 different fresh fruit fillings or keep one for another time. You cover the fruit either with whipped cream, chopped almonds and some cocoa powder or with whipped banana (mixer) and sprinkle chopped or ground hazelnuts on top.

Raw Fruit Cake (for 2 springform pans)

250 g oat flour (8 oz), 350 g wheat flour (12 oz), 90 g buckwheat flour (3 oz), 250 g ground sunflower or linseed oil (8 oz), 300 g water (10 oz), 1 teaspoon cinnamon, 2 teaspoons fennel powder, 1 rasped lemon skin and 1 tablespoon of honey.

For the filling of the cake you can use any type of fresh cut fruit. You can cover the fruit with a cream of whipped banana, hazelnuts and honey.

You mix all the ingredients together and put them into the spring-form pan. Cover this with the fruit of your choice and top it off with the whipped banana cream. This total vegetable-and-fruit cake is best after leaving it alone for 1 day.

Whole Wheat Waffles

Mix 200 g (7 oz) of wheat flour with 250 ml (8 oz) of soya milk, 1 tablespoon of BRAGGS and 1 teaspoon of yeast or baking powder. Leave it for 10 minutes. Butter the waffle iron with oil or butter. Serve the waffles with some fresh jam or a little honey.

Whole Oat, Spelt or Wheat Pancakes

Mix 200 g (7 oz) of wheat flour with 250 ml (8 oz) of soya milk, 1 egg, 1 tablespoon BRAGGS and 1/2 teaspoon of dried celery. Leave it for 10 minutes. Fry the pancakes until they are light brown. For frying you should use a nonstick pan and do the frying without oil or with minute quantities of butter or oil.

Another way: fry some chopped mushrooms and onions briefly in the pan before pouring the pancake batter on top.

Dessert

Here we have our biggest conflict of all. Many people believe that serving fruit is a healthy ending to a nice meal. They believe the dessert should preferably consist of fresh fruit built into some refined creams, puddings or mousse as the final piece of art created by the chef or the homemaker as the climax of a fine meal. From our rules we know that this is out. I am not suggesting discontinuing this type of art, but we have to change the succession, particularly if the dessert contains fresh raw fruit.

Nothing stops us from serving the fruit at the beginning of the meal. You can serve a nice slice of lemon with a piece of lime or orange, beautifully decorated with some other berries, a small portion of whipped cream, a thin slice of smoked salmon, beef or ham, etc. Or serve a nice little fruit basket with a few fresh nuts in the shell. Involve your guest a little in the action and they will appreciate your well-meaning kitchen so much more.

If you however serve some traditional processed products, such as pudding, ice cream, mousse or cake without fresh fruit, you can serve this at the end. But never forget that these processed products are of no value to you but are dead energy that alone rob important vitamins and minerals from your body. You can possibly use a few berries for decoration even if you are breaking the rule. Small quantities will do little or almost no harm.

Always start your meals with fruit or salads. Use your brilliance in this field and you will find that a meal can be a masterpiece without a heavy dessert.

I do not want to discourage anybody from getting treats and pieces of art at the end of a special meal. Keep in mind what is good for you and then if you want to, do this in tiny quantities. The pleasure will be the same without the same consequences.

The listed recipes are a small part of what my family developed over the years.

They are only an inspiration to help you in your own search. Things are not as complex as they look but, as with everything else in life, our own experience will have to be added to make it complete.

I wish you good luck with your journey to a better, more wholesome and fulfilling life.

A Short Summary

I hope that the two excursions we have made together have inspired you to look at your life and at your opportunities from a different angle. We can all, on a daily basis with many small steps, help to reshape our future and even more so create opportunities for our children instead of leaving them destruction.

For me it was a great learning experience to reach to the point that led to the creation of this document. Hopefully this will also encourage you to go on your own direction of exploring your opportunities.

When you do that, don't forget the dreams you did dream when you started out. Without dreaming you will not be able to create the important vision that will lead you to your goals.

You will be what you dream, and you are what you eat!

God bless you! Good luck!